GOOD NEWS FOR PEOPLE WHO HURT

(AND IT IS N.E.A.T!)

REACHING OPTIMUM HEALTH THROUGH

NEURO EMOTIONAL ANTI-SABOTAGE TECHNIQUE

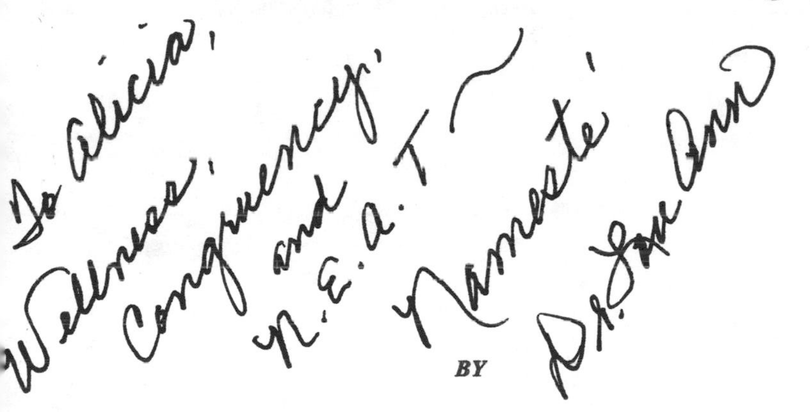

BY

Lou Ann Dickerson Hall, PhD, LPC, LMFT, CDVC, CNET, CCHT

Good News For People Who Hurt
by Dr. Lou Ann Dickerson-Hall

Acknowledgment and appreciation for permission to reprint quotations from the following: Bach, Richard, *Illusions,*Random House, Inc., NY,NY; Chopra, Deepak, *Ageless Body, Timless Mind,* Harmony Books, Crown Pub., Inc., NY, NY; Connelly, Dianne M., *Traditional Acupuncture: The Law of the Five Elements,* Traditional Acupuncture Institute, Columbia, Maryland, Copyright 1979; Dickerson, Laurie, *He Sailed Forth Into the Light;* Dickerson, Hallie Ross, *Dreams;* Justice, Blair, *Who Gets Sick,* Jeremy Tarcher, Inc., Los Angeles, CA, Copyright 1987; Paige, Julie, 1) *Encounter* and 2) *For The Teacher In Each of Us;* Parker, James, 1) *Parker's Principles,* and 2) *The Autonomic System,* Parker College of Chiropractic, Dallas, Tx.; Rossi, Ernest L., and Cheek, David B.,*Mind-Body Therapy,* W. W. Norton & Co., Inc., NY, NY; Saraydarian, Torkim, *The Flame of Beauty, Culture, Love, and Joy,* Aquarian Educational Group, Sedona, AZ; Walker, Scott, NET Inc., Encinitas, CA., (all materials of NET Inc. enclosed)

Fourth Edition: March, 2001; ALL RIGHTS RESERVED

Publisher: Agape' Associates
3734 Clearwell
Amarillo, Texas 79109

Cover Design by Mickey Cathey

Typesetting/Printing by Dallas Offset, Inc., Dallas, TX., USA
Lee Bural

ISBN: 0-9707033-4-1

Editing by: Gene White, Dr. Julie Tooley, and Dan Shapiro

"IF WE VALUE THE PURSUIT OF KNOWLEDGE

WE MUST BE FREE TO FOLLOW WHEREVER

THAT SEARCH MAY LEAD US."

Adlai Stevenson

WARNING: THIS IS NOT A "HOW-TO-DO-IT" BOOK!

THIS BOOK IS WRITTEN FOR THE EXPRESS PURPOSE OF INFORMING THE GENERAL PUBLIC OF THE EXISTENCE OF AND THERAPEUTIC VALUE WITHIN THE NEURO EMOTIONAL TECHNIQUE. (NET)

NET IS A VERY INTRICATE, SCIENTIFIC PROCEDURE. ONLY A HIGHLY TRAINED AND QUALIFIED NET DOCTOR OR LICENSED PROFESSIONAL IS ALLOWED TO TREAT WITH THIS TECHNIQUE.

PREFACE

"Thousands of practitioners in over thirty countries have utilized NET on hundreds of thousands of patients during the last decade. Yet, Dr. Hall's book is the first outreach to educate the general public of the technique's existence. Long overdue, we feel confident this book will inspire suffering patients to gain health through this alternative approach. We salute Dr. Hall for her labor of love on this project."

Drs. Scott and Deborah Walker

TABLE OF CONTENTS

ACKNOWLEDGMENTS

First, last, and always, I want to acknowledge the Source of Life, the Creator.

I want to thank...

...all my teachers, whatever the subject or challenge.

...my beloved parents, Abe and Cleo Dickerson, who gave me life, loved me unconditionally, supported, and always encouraged me through thick and thin, who taught me to laugh, love, and to sing in the face of adversity.

...my dear brother Don, who in life brought me joy and love...and through his death brought me wisdom.

...my beloved children, Mark, Suanne, and Michael, my greatest teachers.

...for all others who have been so lovingly supportive throughout the challenges in writing this book, especially Drs. Scott, Deb, Jane, David, Nell, and Sahna.

...for Aunt Dixie, Kathleen, and Uncle Jeff who prodded me on lovingly whether they knew it or not, with their gifts of humor, wisdom, and laughter.

...for Aunt Ada who has brought a great joy to our family and generously provided her home for the major beginning of this project.

...for Sara, Gene White, Dr. Juli Tooley, and Dan Shapiro for their editorial expertise.

...for all the doctors and patients who generously submitted their case studies and permissions.

...for my former mates, whose privacy I wish to respect by not naming them here, but whose contributions to my life are deeply grasped.

...for Pat, Mary Ann, Evelyn, Linda, Liz, their parents, Bill and Ruby Bublitz, and all other BHS friends who early in life taught me the value of community as did all the Dickerson and Jones families.

...for grandchildren, Christopher, Zachary, and Chloe who bring "genius" to our family.

All the gifts I have received from these, and many more wonderful people, swells my heart as they have shown me that dreams really can come true.

DEDICATION

This book is written in honor and deep appreciation of Drs. Scott and Deborah Walker of Encinitas, California. Dr. Scott Walker is the innovator and developer of *Neuro Emotional Anti-sabotage Technique.* Because of Dr. Deborah's own special gifts, support, and organizational skills, this technique was actually manifested into a reality.

It was through Dr. "Scott's" years of experience as a healthcare provider in chiropractic that he identified repeat patterns of behaviors and/or emotional responses within his patients. These same factors appeared to be related to certain vertebral mis-alignments or neurological abnormalities. In following his keen awareness and curiosity of these repeated occurrences, he began a long extensive study and investigation, which, through his genius, led to the development of this technique.

Dr. "Scott" and Dr. "Deb," we are truly grateful for your commitment, hard work, along with your open, giving, and helping hearts. Because of you both, the world is a better place.

Thank you!

INTRODUCTION

Dr. Scott Walker had successfully and effectively dealt with the structural and biochemical problems of his patients. He later realized, however, that his patients became healthy when their structural, biochemical, and *emotional* components or elements were harmoniously balanced. He viewed this balance as the *Triangle of Health*...with three sides...structural, biochemical, and emotional. He later developed the *Home Run Formula,* covering all the bases with emotions, toxins, biochemistry, and structure.

Dr. Walker's specialty was not counseling people, and even if he had been trained in that specialty, there was no time to add psychological counseling to his practice. The emotional aspects of the problem thus remained "*untouchable.*" The "triangle" was allowed to stay out of balance until he decided to do something about the suspected emotionally based problems of his patients.

After feeling hampered for nearly twenty years of practice, he devoted himself to finding a solution...one that would employ some of the same basic techniques of chiropractic. After years of development and testing, this "solution" arrived. The ongoing result of his work has been the development of this very exciting and powerful new technique. His patients and students call it "a miracle technique." Many health care doctors of all disciplines and training believe the technique to be revolutionary, an icon of future health care. Dr. Walker has been noted for his developments, which many term as "great breakthrough techniques" and was awarded the prestigious national commendation of *"Chiropractor of the Year"* in 1992.

This book is written for you, the individual in pursuit of excellent health, quality of life, inner joy, peace in coping with life's daily challenges, and the ultimate fulfillment of your dreams and goals. This powerful technique creates change, transition, and transformation as it discharges old emotional reality

imprints. This is done cleanly, rapidly, and thoroughly. As Neuro Emotional Complexes (N.E.C.'s) are cleared, they are removed from the human system *not to return unless they are re-imprinted by re-traumatization!*

This book is an attempt to give the reader an overview of this technique. This is not a "how-to" book. This book is intended to provide you with information and therefore the options which will allow you to reclaim your power as a person and whole being. As you are made aware of your options, you can determine for yourself, thereby reclaiming your right of power in determining and partnering in your own health choices.

The first section of this book is primarily dedicated to provide some understanding of the basic philosophy and results of individuals who have experienced the technique. The latter section includes three Addendums which provide more technical, philosophical, and historical aspects of the technique. Patient names have been changed in order to protect their privacy. Some of the practicing physicians have given their written consent to utilize their names as the providers of case studies.

The field of "Energy Medicine" is the wave of the future in health care. NEAT and Chiropractic is energy medicine and yet people who don't already know that are not alerted to that fact. The pharmaceutical and medical thought determines what the "innocent public" thinks of what natural health care is all about.

It is my desire for the world now to become aware of this revolutionary technique...of the powerful, positive impact NET/NEAT can have in our lives, both personally and collectively. The first story is one of my own personal and profound experiences with NEAT.

"EVERY TRUTH PASSES THROUGH THREE

STAGES BEFORE IT IS RECOGNIZED.

IN THE FIRST, IT IS RIDICULED,

IN THE SECOND, IT IS OPPOSED,

IN THE THIRD, IT IS REGARDED

AS SELF-EVIDENT."

Arthur Schopenhauer

GOOD NEWS FOR PEOPLE WHO HURT!

CHAPTER ONE

"Dreams are like bubbles,
That glimmer and shine,
As they grow in proportion,
But no trace can we find.
Of the rainbow of colors,
As it bursts in the air,
Only a drop of water
To show it was there.

Bubbles bring laughter
To the heart of a child,
And dreams to the youth,
So often beguile,
For like bubbles of childhood,
They burst in the air
With only a teardrop
To show they were there."

~ Hallie Ross Dickerson

* * * * * * * * * * * *

I was extremely privileged to be present as my only sibling, big brother Don, made his transition in death. There on that sterile

hospital bed was the man who had been so full of the life force energy, a very creative and successful architect, sensitive and caring, a loving husband, father, brother, uncle, nephew, and friend to many. Now this very vital man was wasting away before our eyes to the monstrous cancer!

How deeply we felt he was much too young for this to be happening to him. We resisted the inevitable truth. How could the breath of life be snatched away from one so full of life? He had too many more mountains to climb, so much more laughter to laugh, thousands of miles to travel, beautiful buildings to design, and Christmases to share with his grandchildren. We were not prepared to let him go!

Time stood still in that softly lit hospital room while his favorite musical tapes softly played in the background. As the busy oncology nurses entered the room from time to time to care for his needs, they would suddenly stop, take a deep breath, and to our surprise, comment, "It feels so wonderful in this room!" as though realizing they were in the presence of deep, profound love and beauty. Perhaps this would seem odd, given the circumstances. Obviously, a very transformative, though painful and difficult, event was taking place. Though his body was wasting away, it was also as if all of his suffering in the previous months had cleared away all the human entrapments of insecurity, fear, and forgetfulness that block us all from the knowledge of who we really are.

Don's children played his favorite recording of Handel's *"Hallelujah Chorus"* from the *Messiah*. Although in a coma, suddenly the expression of deep, intense joy and ecstasy came across Don's face. It was so astonishing that when first noticed, his son exclaimed, "Look at Dad's face!" We were all astounded, yet deeply comforted, and somehow lifted to indescribable heights with him!

After the last "Hallelujah!" had echoed in the room, ever so gently with that beautiful expression on his face, our beloved took his last breath and quietly slipped from us. Hand in hand, ringed about his bed, we offered, one by one, our prayers and utterances of deeply felt gratitude for the life of this one who had so richly touched and blessed our lives.

It was a sacred moment, and we all knew without a doubt that we were in the presence of the Divine. For a moment, time stood still as our deepest fears, sadness, and insecurities seemed to disappear. I have never felt more love. We were all lifted from our heavy hearts to a place of holiness that mere words do not adequately describe.

Riding on the elevator as we left the hospital that night, his loving wife broke our silence as she stated:

> **"I know tomorrow I will probably express my tears**
> **and sadness, but for now, I am ecstatic with the beautiful**
> **experience of the past hour!"**

We all understood.

In Rosemary Altea's book *Proud Spirit*, Grey Eagle is quoted as saying regarding death:

> ***"You approach with uncertainty. And yet, all there is here is light... and yet all there is, is joy... and yet all there is, is beauty."***

It is with deep abiding gratitude that I walked that journey with him.

Don was the last surviving member of my family of origin and as we had always experienced a close, fun, and loving relationship, this loss was understandably, tremendously difficult for me. In the months that followed his death, I was both the participant and observer of my own deep grief. With the beautiful experience at the time of his death, I found it dichotomous, confusing, as though divided into two parts, puzzled at the depth of my grief, and at the same time, still feeling the ecstasy of those last moments.

Most of my life, I had been blessed with excellent health. However, soon after Don's death, my physical body appeared to be falling apart, and I became quite ill. Never had I been in such despair and pain. Many mornings, I would have to roll off the bed because I could not get up due to the physical pain. I was diagnosed with Lyme's Disease, Fibromyalgia, and it was suspicioned that I also had Lupus. All of these are "incurable" diseases in modern medicine.

As an experienced therapist, I utilized every known grieving therapeutic process. I spoke and "therapized" with other therapists. I journaled, sobbed, screamed into my pillow, did Elizabeth Kubler-Ross' "mattress work," ran the Neuro Linguistic Programming "Grief Pattern," self-hypnosis, and many other therapies, but without success. There was no relief. The weariness of it all was indescribably unbearable.

Four months later I went, under protest, to the 1994 NET SUCCESS in Montana. This was at the insistence of my NET Buddy, Dr. Jane Lock. (NET SUCCESS is a seminar Dr. Walker conducts, which he subtitles "Physician Heal Thyself" through NEAT.)

I had struggled with the decision of whether or not I could go, if I was even capable of physically managing the long 2,000 mile flight. Jane had sent me nutritional supplements to assist in the clearing of the diagnosed illnesses. With this help, I then experienced enough relief that I began to feel some hope.

My body still ached so severely with pain, however, and there were times it literally took all my determination to rise from a chair, the bed, or even to walk. The trip was a long and excruciatingly painful experience. I was ever so grateful when finally I arrived at Flathead Lake Lodge where the seminar was held.

The first day of the seminar, my friend, Jane, began the NEAT with me, and the long prayed for miracles began. For three days, she and other doctors uncovered and cleared old NECs of deep grief and

loss from my first marriage… grief and loss which I, as a therapist, had processed for so long… loss I thought had been resolved years earlier but was, in fact, still held within my body!

> **(Note: One might assume the NECs were all about the recent loss of my brother. It is important to understand, however, that though I was presently grieving Don's death, his loss triggered old, different, unresolved emotions {NECs} from the past.)**

Time and time again, NECs were uncovered in my lung meridian points of "grief." One NEC was at the age of three when my beloved dog and constant companion, Pogo, had to be taken away by my father because Pogo was killing the neighbor's chickens. As an adult I can understand the rationale of this action, but at that age I only understood that my beloved pet and best friend was taken from me. This had been traumatic for me emotionally.

After so many NECs were cleared from the lung meridian access points (MAP), the emotion of "lost" was discovered in the heart meridian access point (MAP), when my grandfather, Daddy Bill, also died a slow, agonizing, cancerous death. My gall bladder and liver meridians held "anger" imprinted at the age of thirty-one due to a relationship loss through infidelity and emotional abuse.

These NECs and many more were stacked one atop another from old experiences, long forgotten, all stored away, but nevertheless

imprinted... and each one piled atop another, impacting my entire system in the present grief and loss!

The results following the clearing of all those NECs were amazing! In just four days, I was *physically, mentally, emotionally, and spiritually pain-free!* It was there on the fifth day of that 1994 NET SUCCESS I committed myself to the writing of this book.

Later, back home, my doctors were puzzled by this complete health reversal! I had prayed for a miracle and had received many. There were no medical explanations other than perhaps there had been mistaken diagnoses.

In the time since that 1994 NET SUCCESS I have, of course, missed my dear brother and grieved the loss of his embodiment. The difference, however, is that there has been a deep undergirding of strength and peace, a gratitude for our life together, the joy and laughter of remembered play, and multitudes of other gifts experienced as his sister. Additionally, none of the symptoms of those diseases have reappeared.

I have, as a result of NEAT, reclaimed a deep passion for life and an inner sense of purpose, love, and divine guidance. Daily I feel such deep gratitude, amazement, and awe for this powerful healing tool, to share it with my patients, and to be a participant in their miracles with NET/NEAT.

What perfection it is that this gift has been given to us at such a time in the history of humanity! As a dear friend often exclaims,

without irreverence regarding the divine scheme of things:

"Isn't God cute!"

* * * * * * * * * * *

BOBBY'S STORY

Bobby was a bright, handsome, eight year old boy. His parents were both teachers. They brought him for treatment due to a disturbing, dramatic, and very sudden change in his behavior two months earlier. They reported Bobby had previously been a straight "A" student and really liked school. As a popular boy, he had many peer and adult friends... an extrovert who loved people.

Recently, however, Bobby had developed a deep anxiety and personality change that was very disturbing to all who knew and loved him. Almost overnight, he no longer wanted to attend school, his grades dropped drastically, and he experienced nightmares on a regular basis.

His worried, puzzled, yet loving parents further reported he had become very shy, introverted, and would not go into the school building without clinging to his mother's skirt, sometimes crying. These behaviors were all very unlike the boy they had known the previous eight years.

An adult friend of the family observed this drastic change in Bobby's behavior and school performance. Quite concerned and familiar with the NEAT process, she referred Bobby for treatment.

As Bobby entered my office, he held his head down and averted eye contact. He shyly shook my hand and insisted his parents do all the talking. His little hands trembled as he sat on the couch close to his mother. At one point, he fought back the tears as his parents related his history and their deep worry and concern about the sudden unexplained change in him. Neither Bobby, nor his parents, could give any answers or insight into the source of the changes. Finally Bobby spoke, blurting out in a quivering voice, "I want to feel and be the way I used to be!"

Utilizing the NEAT, I asked Bobby to recall the feeling he experienced when he entered his classroom at school. His little face flushed, he trembled, and I worked quickly.

The emotion of "paralyzed will" (feeling stuck) was discovered stored in the left kidney meridian access point. The original imprint of this emotion occurred when his new female teacher made a practice of taking the boys to the bathroom and standing inside the door watching them urinate. "This was," she explained later, "to make sure the boys did not misbehave in the bathroom."

Bobby had been particularly sensitive to her stern manner and voice in this practice. He trembled again when this was verbalized. Bobby flushed as he stated, "I didn't like for her to watch!" As he had

always been a well-behaved child, her behavior was beyond his comprehension and he interpreted this act as a violation of his privacy. As the tears pooled in his eyelids, the Neuro Emotional Complex (NEC) of "paralyzed will" was discharged and followed by post-testing.

Bobby experienced an immediate release of anxiety. His facial expression changed to a smile as he exclaimed, *"Hey! This is NEAT!"* I responded with a smile, stating, "Yes, Bobby, this IS NEAT!... and it is called Neuro Emotional Anti-sabotage Technique." He laughed, and it was only then that I observed the boy who was previously described as his "natural" spontaneous personality and behavior.

Bobby exuberantly and in rapid succession "fired away" questions about the technique, stating he really felt good and like his "old self" again. No *longer* did he avoid eye contact, nor hang his head shyly. He spoke with confidence and natural spontaneity, then smiled and hugged his mother. Both parents were stunned! Finally, his mother exclaimed, "We don't understand what you just did, but we do know that somehow a miracle just happened. You have given us back our son! Yes, Bobby is right, *this is NEAT!*"

Bobby post-tested strongly with statements concerning, "OKAY allowing myself to do my best in all areas," "OKAY speaking up for myself when I am uncomfortable with the teacher watching in the bathroom," and "OKAY and safe making friends easily." He was

even strong on "OKAY with my teacher," indicating he was free from the sabotaging emotion.

So if the filtering screens of our perception were cleared, then everything would appear to us as it is… INFINITE…!

William Blake

And so our perceptual fields *can* be cleared, and we can become free, boundless, limitless, and empowered!

* * * * * * * * * * *

Now you must be thinking something like, "How is it possible for something so traumatic and debilitating as Bobby's experience (for him) to be discharged or cleared so quickly?" or "Is it even logical for us to think that we could be happy, productive, and free, unencumbered by our self-sabotaging behaviors and feelings?" These are very good questions and the answers may be found within the Neuro Emotional Anti-sabotaging Technique (NEAT).

So, how does this work?

First of all, imagine your body as being the most sophisticated computer system ever developed. Most of us are aware that computers store what we choose to store, by striking the "save" button on the keyboard. What would you think if you were told that *everything* you have *ever* experienced is "stored" somewhere

within your body system? In much the same way we "save" a program on our computers via a disk copy, so have our "body systems" (sub-conscious) recorded and saved our every experience.

These "stored" emotions then condition our responses to the present time, place, relationships, and circumstances. The emotions that sabotage us are called "Neuro Emotional Complexes," or NECs, for short. Dr. Walker defines the NEC as:

> ***"A subjective maladaptation syndrome adopted by the human organism in response to a real or perceived threat to any aspect of its survival."***

(The NEC will be discussed more at length later.)

At any given point in our personal history, we can be imprinted (conditioned) with an NEC if our system is vulnerable in any way... physically, emotionally, or mentally. Simply put, two people could have the same experience, but only one would be imprinted with the NEC.

Once the NEC is present and in place, from that point on until discharged (cleared), we will be controlled to some degree by the NEC. This is much in the same way the puppeteer pulls the strings, so does the NEC sabotage and control us (from the subconscious)!

Furthermore, these NECs, once in place, will repeatedly attract the "likeness" to the NEC through experiences in the present. Some examples:

1. **Setting high goals, such as reaching an income of $50,000 this year and never attaining that goal.**
2. **Vowing to never marry another abusive, alcoholic person, only to attract and be attracted to those personalities.**
3. **Determining to be more patient and kind to your children and spouse, only to hear yourself yelling and screaming at them again!**

These are simple examples of the sabotaging nature of the NECs. When we search for and identify the earliest, original event in which the NEC was imprinted into our system, the sabotaging emotion is quickly, simply, and thoroughly cleared... in much the same way we click the "delete" button on the computer with those programs we no longer want nor need!

Additionally, in the same way with your computer you might check to see if the program you deleted is gone, NEAT post-checks to ascertain if the body system is cleared of the NEC. Whereas prior to the NEAT clearing process, the *muscles went weak* (please refer to pages 22 and 259 which explain more about muscle testing) while the

person held a picture in his/her mind of the event or felt the emotion. After the clearing, the muscles are strong!

We are all aware of the polygraph test (lie detector test), and the fact that it is not considered to be completely reliable, and therefore not admissible in court, though it is used often in law agencies for "indicators" of truth or untruths. Through the lie detector test and muscle testing, we are gauging the responses of the body to certain stimuli. The major difference between the two, however, is that the LDT is looking for the historical truth of the testee. In other words, a sociopath taking the LDT could pass it and show no reaction to a question like, "Did you murder Jack?" This is because the sociopath has no conscience or feeling of being attached to the event of murdering Jack, even when he/she committed the act!

It is very important to be aware that in the process of NEAT, we are looking for the *emotional reality*, not necessarily the *historical reality!* The emotional reality is defined as "that which is perceived, felt, or believed to be true." (Please see Pg. 225 Emotional/Historical Reality)

Most of us are motivated to be happy. Our pursuits, goals, and well-laid plans are motivated because we believe if we attain success in any given arena (i.e., a Divine Right partner, financial success, or cabin in the woods), these things will make us happy.

How often have we attained our goals and still felt unhappy? Or, how often have we failed to attain our goals, even though we have

thoroughly spent our energies and intentions, affirmed, dreamed, and exercised our thorough plans? The well-intentioned New Year's resolutions to start an exercise program, lose weight, cut down on alcohol consumption, eat healthier, spend more quality time with the family, and make more money have so often gone awry. This is all because of what we might term the "puppeteer" pulling our strings, in charge of us, sabotaging our dreams, so to speak! We think we are in charge (consciously), but in fact, we are not!

In the case of Bobby, who had experienced for the most part a successful and happy life, a traumatic experience with the teacher violating his space created the Neuro Emotional Complex. This is the recording or imprint in Bobby's subconscious, thereafter controlling his feelings, behaviors, energy, and sabotaging his health, emotions, and highest success.

Sigmund Freud first introduced us to the concept of the subconscious. The general thought today among those in the psychotherapeutic professions is that the majority of our actions *are* due to the subconscious, and what has been recorded there. In other words, the subconscious is in charge! As most of our actions, impulses, and behaviors are outside of our conscious awareness, we are not aware of what makes us feel and do the things we do. In essence we are held "captive" or imprisoned by the NECs! Over a long period of time, these feelings and behaviors become the norm for us, and we get the repeated unwanted results (i.e. self-sabotage).

So, you ask, "Just what is NEAT, and how does it work?" Neuro Emotional Anti-sabotage Technique (heretofore referred to as NEAT) is a technique expanded from the Neuro Emotional Technique (NET).

> **(NOTE: NET is a methodology of finding and removing neurological or physical aberrations {Neuro Emotional Complexes} in the human organism. NET seeks to normalize the pattern of emotional trauma in the presence of neurological deficit. Essentially, NET is a system of neurological correction.)**

NEAT is about *helping people.* It is about relieving suffering. It is about clearing old emotional trauma which has been fixated or attached, in the body. These old fixated traumas (NECs) have created self-sabotage, blocking the roads to successful living. The old axiom, "Why do I do the things I don't want to do, and why don't I do the things I want to do?" is an example of NECs creating self-sabotage.

Bobby did not want to have the nightmares, lower his grades at school, be frightened to leave his mother's side, or be shy and frightened. Try as he did, he could not control nor stop his feelings and behaviors which were so different from before.

What we feel about ourselves becomes our truth, and then our behavior matches and acts out that truth. When Bobby's teacher stood watching in the boy's bathroom, he was traumatized because (for him) that violated his privacy. From that experience, he felt

unsafe in his world. For the other boys, perhaps it did not. With his system somehow vulnerable, his trauma imprinted or fixated into his body, more specifically in his left kidney meridian.

For five thousand years the Chinese have recognized the link between emotions and the physical body. They understood the organs of the body are capable of storing emotions which have traumatized the individual. Additionally, they also understood that certain emotions are stored in individual organ meridians. (Pg. 240 Organ Meridian System and Emotions)

So how was the NEC found in Bobby? Dr. Walker discovered that when the subconscious sends a message that conflicts with the conscious mind, a strong muscle will weaken.

After preliminary testing of Bobby making statements obviously true for him emotionally, such as "My name is Bobby," and "I love my parents," Bobby's arm muscle went weak on the statement of "I'm OKAY with my teacher." That was the indicator his subconscious was not congruent or aligned with the conscious statement, thereby indicating an NEC was present.

Next, Bobby was asked to just think of his teacher. Simultaneously, I touched each of the organ meridian access points in order to locate the position of the stored emotion. His arm muscle temporarily went weak on each point until the left kidney meridian access point was touched. When the muscle became strong, this indicated the emotion was stored there. It could have been one of many emotions, such as

dread, fear, miffed, but when the emotion of "paralyzed will" (stuck) was voiced, Bobby's arm went weak. This was the tip-off there was a "charge" on it. He was not congruent with the statement.

Through the muscle testing, the event with his teacher indicated Bobby was imprinted (through his perceptual field of emotional reality) with the NEC of "paralyzed will" or "stuck." As Bobby thought about and remembered the picture of that event, the clinical procedures were used to discharge the NEC. Thus, the emotional block that could have remained "stuck" in Bobby's subconscious for years causing untold damage to his quality of life was discharged... in one session!

NECs are physical abnormalities. NET/NEAT is not psychotherapy, talk-it-out therapy, or hypnotherapy. All these therapies can resolve issues. They can also take years. NET/NEAT works almost instantly to release sabotaging NECs stored in the physical body. As with Bobby, the patient can then move on to more productive behavior responses. His subconscious now matches his conscious mind, and that's when great results occur.

Three years later, Bobby continues to be the successful straight "A" student. He enjoys his many friends, sports, remains the outgoing extrovert, and never meets a "stranger!" This beautiful bright child is now free of the debilitating NEC. He is free to unfold again, to grow, to explore, to become and be all that he can be.

As pertains to Bobby and all others who are traumatized, then returned to their former selves, Rev. Doug Manning of Oklahoma City, Oklahoma has said:

"God created you,
It was Beauty.
It was Good.
He smiled.
He was pleased.
Another Masterpiece
By the Hands of the Master."

My daily prayer is that we each be the Masterpiece we are created to be.

* * * * * * * * * * * *

CHAPTER TWO

INTRODUCTION TO NEAT/NET

To paraphrase Victor Hugo:

> ***"Nothing in this world is as powerful***
> ***as an idea whose time has come."***

One Monday morning, I received a phone call from my personal physician. He was frantic, stating he had an emergency with a patient and requested I come over immediately. When I told him that my patient schedule was filled for the day and I could not get away, he persisted. He quickly reported he had a thirty-four year old female patient in his office who had become hysterical upon recall of repressed memories of childhood physical, emotional, and sexual abuse.

His first patient of the day was this woman named Sue. When he began the NET process with her, her recall had instantaneously occurred, followed by her hysteria. He related some of her memories that she could express, and then I understood his serious and frantic concern!

After reassuring him and offering suggestions for the present crisis, I agreed to see her during my lunch hour. My curiosity was

peaked about a technique that could so easily and quickly access such deep repressed memories. (He had not utilized hypnosis, psychotherapy, nor psychotropic drugs to access those memories stored for years in the unconscious mind.)

At noon Sue sat before me, obviously still quite disturbed as evidenced by her crying, trembling, and shallow breathing. Her recalled stories unfolded before me. The memories at times were quite detailed, and others were more vague. The atrocities she had experienced were some of the most grotesque, inhumane, and vile with which I had ever worked or studied. I was convinced of her truth in recall of these horrid repressed memories.

Thus began my journey into the world of NEAT/NET. Intrigued, I flew the following weekend to Detroit, Michigan for my first basic training course.

I was skeptical, cautious, and dubious as I waited to learn of this procedure that elicited Sue's repressed memories.

After a brief introduction and explanation of the technique, Dr. Walker asked for a demonstration volunteer. He selected an individual with the most difficult and, I presumed, the most challenging problem. I was impressed with his courage. Some two hundred doctors filled the seminar room, observing intently.

Utilizing muscle testing, (sometimes referred to as applied kinesiology), Dr. Walker began the NET process with Jerry.

(NOTE: Muscle testing is the access to the body system's computer and is utilized in detecting and diagnosing the location of a physiologically held Neuro Emotional Complex. Present research indicates muscle testing is very accurate.)

Dr. Kris Peterson of Hermiston, Oregon, concluded in a controlled double blind study that:

> **"When musculoskeletal and attentional variables are controlled for, muscle testing is a sensitive, significantly reliable tool in detecting adverse emotional arousal in response to threat stimuli."**

> **(Muscle testing will be discussed more in depth later.)**

Transfixed, I observed Dr. Walker's work with intense fascination and curiosity. My skepticism waned significantly as I observed the rapid-fire, laser-like "detective" work the doctor performed in eliciting information from Jerry's body, not consciously known at times to Jerry himself.

The initial question Dr. Walker had posed to the group of some two hundred doctors was, "Is anyone present who is unhappy with his or her practice?" Jerry reported:

"Yes! I am unhappy about my practice! I am forty-five years old and was forced to give up my practice due to severe cardiac disease. I have always adhered to good health practices. I have maintained an excellent diet, regularly exercised, never smoked, and have lead a relatively stress-free lifestyle. There is no history of cardiac disease in my family… and no one can tell me why I have it, nor how to reverse it!"

Dr. Walker proceeded with him ever so gently. Back into history they journeyed with the NET process. The NEC was located in the heart meridian. It was discovered that before Jerry was born, he experienced an *emotional reality* that he had been a twin, and that his twin brother had not survived. (This phenomenon is known as the Vanishing Twin Syndrome {VTS}.)

(NOTE: Medical science has long been aware of the rather common multiple gestations that eventually result in the survival of only one fetus. Until now, however, no one has considered the emotional impact the loss of a sibling in-utero could produce within the surviving fetus until Dr. Walker and others using this technique began repeatedly discovering this phenomenon.

Additionally, when discovered, the emotional impact is usually very traumatic, as observed in Jerry's case.)

At the point of this discovery, Jerry began to cry. He was both puzzled and somewhat embarrassed at this own emotional reaction in the presence of so many of his peers!

Dr. Walker cleared the NECs of "lost," "vulnerable," "abandoned," and "deserted"... all located in the heart meridian. (It was later that I learned that NECs left untreated long enough in an organ meridian access point will weaken and eventually create disease in that organ!)

Dr. Walker instructed Jerry to 1) picture the time in-utero when his twin brother died, 2) hold with one hand the forehead where the emotional points are located, 3) hold with the other hand the heart meridian point, 4) breathe deeply upon his command, while Dr. Walker 5) adjusted the thoracic vertebrae(s).

My advanced certification in Neuro Linguistic Programming had developed and honed my skills of reading individual's verbal and non-verbal responses. As I observed the entire NET process, it was obvious to me that something *significant* had taken place within Jerry!

The results were unmistakable! His skin tone and color changed. His breathing pattern shifted to a more relaxed and even flow. The voice changed to a melodic even meter, and the posture became

more erect! Jerry, no longer tearful, commented about how amazed he was at the difference he felt within himself as he dazedly walked back to his seat.

A year later I met Jerry at another NET/NEAT training. He was the picture of health as he radiantly announced not only had he astonished his cardiologist with his recovery (from a coronary disease that was reportedly incurable), but also that he was working in his private practice on a two-thirds time basis, doing very well, and projecting within the next six months, he would be completely recovered and back to a full time practice!

* * * * * * * * * * *

Following that training, I returned to Amarillo. It was then that the real work began with my physician's patient, Sue. Her most interesting journey back to health was accomplished through conjoint weekly psychotherapy and NEAT treatment.

The results with Sue were phenomenal! Within five months, this bright young lady calmly and courageously confronted the perpetrators of her abuse. She spoke her truth to them of her experiences, was met with vehement denials, and yet she remained strong and calm. She now owns and maintains a successful business, has returned to a university, studying to become a psychotherapist and hopefully, a NET/NEAT Practitioner.

My years of experience and training had taught me that to come to Sue's level of resolution would have taken years of traditional intensive psychotherapy. My beliefs (with supportive data) were firmly held that this short period of recovery was impossible, especially given the depth of her trauma. The evidence, however, was contrary to this concept, for she was rapidly and radically helped by NEAT/NET in dramatic life-changing ways which she confirmed by stating:

"I now, for the first time in my life, am really living!"

* * * * * * * * * * *

CHAPTER THREE

OUR CHALLENGE

"Truth has to fall on fertile soil."

Gift of the Red Bird

~ Paula D'Arcy

Man's inhumanity to man unfortunately is a truism. It is not Truth, however. There is a difference. A truism is a fact, something that almost everyone knows or believes. It is an action, a practice, or condition. It is a truism in that millions of people were cruelly slaughtered, gassed, defamed, starved, and treated in every other non-human form during Hitler's reign in Europe. It is a truism that the United States has fifty states. It is a truism that rape, murder, dishonesty, deceit, hatred, and betrayal occur everyday in our world. It is a truism that the sun rises in the east, and sets in the west.

Truth, on the other hand, is that which is true. Truth is a higher form. It is based on more than what is normally known or understood. It is ethereal. Truth is a state of *being*. It is a truth that we were born perfectly programmed to focus on love. We came into this world as *blueprints of the Divine*. We were born

creative, inquisitive, spontaneous, and living in a world full of imagination, enchantment, and hope. An example of our fond, yet often unconscious, remembrances of that Truth is the following:

In a coliseum filled with two thousand people, a highly charged, energetic, and interesting speaker holds the rapt attention of the audience. A toddler breaks free from her mother's care and wanders innocently onto the stage. Where then goes the focus of two thousand people? The answer is, of course, to the precious toddler who symbolizes our faint memories of the "Being" we once were… and still *who we really are*, though perhaps suffocating from the collected fears of experience.

So what happened? As we grew and were exposed to a seemingly larger world, instead of focusing on love, we were taught to become a "cardboard self." To survive, we too often became what others wanted us to be. To be safe we had to learn we could not trust our creative selves. We learned it was not safe to be our spontaneous, inquisitive, and delightful selves, but that we must take care of other's needs, to please others and, in the process, lose ourselves! We were taught to see and experience a world that contradicts who we really are! We learned jealousy, hate, separation, exclusivity, greed, lying, ugliness, pride, and criticism. In short, we learned *fear*! In her book, *A Return to Love*, Marianne Williamson reflects on the *Course in Miracles*. She emphasizes the point that we were born with love, and it is fear that we learned here.

It is the unlearning and relinquishing of this fear that is the Truth of our spiritual journey. Williamson expounds on the profound thought, to paraphrase, that love is empirical fact, and our purpose is to become consciously aware of that fact. To experience the meaning of life is to experience love, both in others and within ourselves. To remember that we *are love* is our purpose here on earth.

Our beautiful Mother Earth and yes, humanity, now stands on the precipice of either great calamity or a new birthing. We are being called to return to who we are. We are being confronted daily with the challenges of our unresolved griefs, mournings, losses, fears, and traumas.

In the tragic death of Lady Diana, the world responded with an outpouring of deep, unmitigated grief. Is there not one of us who could not identify with some point in her history, whether it be the "princess story" archetype our daughters are taught to dream about, her childhood growing up with divorced parents, her becoming a princess only to suffer a broken heart, her public humiliation, infidelity, divorce, loss of title, feeling of being all alone amidst those she felt did not understand her, or the struggle with her own demons of depression and anorexia?

And yet, she rose above all that and more. With the indomitable spirit of caring, she reached out her hand to her suffering human

family, stepping forward into life, powerfully, and completely with who and what she was! With *this* we can also identify!

As the world was transfixed in the loss of Lady Diana, another beloved humble one, often called "Saint," quietly slipped from us also. Mother Teresa, by her very life, exemplified love and service for humanity.

In these momentous events, glued to the multimedia, our hearts responded with a "knowing." For without a therapist, minister, rabbi, priest, or friend, we were (consciously or unconsciously) reminded of all our own personal unresolved pains from our past. Yes, there was a chord that struck a common note within us all!

We have been given life, but we have not really lived. We have been called to freedom, but we do not live as free souls. We have found anxiety painful and thus returned to our personal lies and illusions about ourselves. At some point we have known life to be good, but then renounced hope in the midst of our despair.

Knowing that life is given to us only in the present, we cling desperately to the past with all our fears. We then project those fears and imagined fantasies into the future, thereby blocking us from "Being" in the present! Knowing at some level that we are received in "Being" as we really are, we have not chosen to "Be" the great *"I AM!"*

In dying to our old false dreaming and vain struggles, centering our lives in that Power beyond us, we are given new possibilities for

living. We are accepted by that which is greater than we. This means that whatever we have done or will ever do, nothing can change the fact that we are in this world, and that even now we can dare to "Be" the Divine Blueprint that we are!

Peace will come to this world when peace resides within the hearts of each of us. We are being called collectively, as well as individually, to awaken, to release our fears, of feeling like the victim, to resolve our mourning, angers, and resentments, to forgive ourselves and others. We must once again be authentic, reclaim that Divine Spark within, remember that we are spiritually connected, and then return to *Love*. NEAT can help us respond to that call. The future is open and this is the one everlasting truth... may we be courageous, open our hearts, and receive this gift and *Live!*

* * * * * * * * * * *

CHAPTER FOUR

NET/NEAT HEALING GRIEF AND LOSS

"What the caterpillar calls the end of life,
the Master calls a butterfly."

~ Richard Bach

Grief and loss, simply put, are but a part of the human condition. No one escapes the pain of loss, whether it be loss of a job, loss of a dream, loss of self, loss of a beloved through death or divorce, loss of health, loss of youth, or loss of money and prestige.

Most of us fear the unknown and what appears to be an all embracing darkness in the process of death. Although most world religions espouse and teach belief in an eternal or afterlife, our fear-based behavior often belies that belief, and thus our health, relationships, and living are diminished.

At issue here, however, is that although we may have chosen to live free of all the entrapments of unresolved grief, all too often we have no conscious thought of grief, or of any of the other emotions (anger, guilt, denial, shock) that are all a part of the grieving process.

Dr. Elizabeth Kubler-Ross first identified these other emotions in her research and book *On Death and Dying*. She relates her own personal experience with unconscious grief and its impact upon her life in the following story.

*** * * * * * * * * * ***

At the age of fifty, Dr. Ross was conducting a workshop on Unconditional Love. A minister who coordinated the event had unknowingly "pushed her buttons." Her reaction to this man was intense anger and resentment for which she had no understanding!

Feeling these emotions intensely, she struggled to make it through the week-long workshop. Doing her best, she "put the lid" on these emotions triggered by this man. Totally puzzled, she pursued this mystery and was determined to uncover why her reaction to him had been so potent!

The workshop was held during the Easter holidays, a time in which she did not want to be away from her family. She was met at the Chicago airport, and the mystery began to unravel when her psychiatrist colleagues asked her to tell them about the seminar and the "Easter Bunnies."

This was a seemingly simple request. However, she shocked herself with her reply of intense agitation by making several irritable comments. She finished with, "*... and don't you ever, <u>ever</u> talk to me again about Easter Bunnies!*" Immediately she burst into

tears, having no idea why, with her brain limping weakly behind. She sobbed in agony for the next eight hours!

Eventually, she began to recall the initial events leading to her puzzling reactions. As one of a set of triplet sisters, Dr. Ross had felt "cloned." Being identical, she and her sisters were dressed alike, given the same name initials by their father, and even suspected that her parents and teachers alike never knew to whom they were relating. Her truth was that one sister was always on her mother's lap, the other sister always on her father's lap, and there was no third lap for her in which to be held and loved.

She sought refuge and unconditional love in the rabbits which the family raised. As her father was a thrifty Swiss man, this was considered a way of providing food (unknown to little Elizabeth) for his family.

Everyone in the family had their chores, and she was delighted that hers was to care for the rabbits. They became her "love objects." She fed them, watered them, loved them, and they returned that love in full measure.

When she was sad and lonely, needing to cry, she buried her face in their soft fur, and they loved her unconditionally. When she needed someone to talk to, she talked to them. When she needed a hug, they snuggled close to her. Her rabbits came to her and responded as they would to no one else. She felt special and an

individual person to them. Her most treasured time was spent with her beloved rabbits.

The time came, however, when she was told by her father to pick one of the rabbits to take down the mountain to the butcher! Her agony of this ordeal was indescribable! How could she pick one of her beloved rabbits to be eaten by her family?! On the other hand, as a good six-year-old Swiss child, how could she disobey her father? It was impossible!

Eventually, she stoically obeyed him. Later, however, as she observed the family consuming her beloved rabbit at the dinner table, she felt them to be cannibals!

As time went on, she was instructed to carry another rabbit, and then another, and another. One by one she carried them down the mountain to the butcher shop. Each one was traumatically difficult, until the last, her favorite of all, her beloved Blackie was left.

She went to Blackie and begged him to run away, promising she would find and feed him in the woods. But this was not to be, Blackie loved her and would not leave her. She looked for excuses, an "out." She procrastinated but finally resolved to be the obedient child.

Finally, with a broken heart, she carried him down the mountain. She waited in miserable silence outside the shop, as always, for the package of raw meat that she would deliver to her mother's kitchen.

When the butcher stepped outside to hand her the package of raw meat, she was stunned when the butcher exclaimed, "Damn shame you had to bring this one! In a few days *she would have had little bunnies!"*

As a little girl, it was the most devastating experience of her life! She could not express her rage or deep sorrow. She could not let her family know how vulnerable she was. She believed it would kill her! Little Elizabeth carried the package of raw meat back up the mountain like a zombie, never to express her emotions surrounding this experience, and never to have bunnies again!

For the next fifty years, every time she saw who she perceived to be a cheap man or a penny-pincher, she had to put the lid on her emotions tighter and tighter and tighter... until one day it was uncorked by the minister who innocently symbolized (a cheap man) to her subconscious and triggered the imprint (NEC) of so long ago! She adds:

> ***"In all my advanced professional training,***
> ***no one had ever talked about 'bunnies'!"***

Dr. Ross processed her rage and grief with her method of mattress work. She reports she can now see a cheap man, not be affected, and recognize that it is his problem and not hers.

*** * * * * * * * * * ***

An NEC can "seemingly" lie dormant for a protracted period of time. This "seemingly" is a tongue-in-cheek verbiage. The NEC remaining within the system, non-neutralized, will eventually create disease within the host organ meridian. When this topic was discussed in NET/NEAT training, a NET buddy turned to me and exclaimed:

"No wonder we fall apart when we get older!!"

An interesting case follows which demonstrates this phenomenon.

* * * * * * * * * * *

MONA

Mona reported enjoying good health most of her life. When she developed severe and chronic bladder pain in her mid-twenties, she was baffled. She had suffered a few bladder and urinary tract infections, so naturally assumed these had weakened and had paved the way for a severe condition.

Examinations and tests revealed no infection. A mystery surrounded her condition. None of the doctors could find anything wrong, and there was no explanation for her intense pain. The only

treatments offered her were antidepressant drugs to combat what they implied was an imaginary illness.

No doctor had asked her what she thought or felt, or about anything that was going on in her life that may have contributed to this illness or to the now developed anxiety. She accepted all this due to her previous experience of doctors being detached and unavailable to open communication. However, after three years of going from bad to worse, she was ready to try anything.

By the time she sought alternative health care she was really frightened. She could barely sleep at night and, as a result was severely depressed and tense. When she finally called an acupuncturist from China, she was in tears and desperate.

As the acupuncturist warned, the "needling" technique was intense. Mona reported feeling strong electrical shocks running up and down her body as the doctor applied the needles to the very precise meridian points. It was not pleasant, but it did not hurt, either. She felt almost complete relief for a few days.

Mona had to pay for these sessions out of her pocket because her insurance did not cover this treatment. She did experience temporary relief from the intense pain.

After approximately a year of ups and downs, Mona began her care with an American acupuncturist who was very warm and communicative. She made special efforts to get to know Mona as a person, which she claimed helped her a great deal with her diagnosis.

It was very comforting and relieving to Mona to be able to talk with someone who would not only listen carefully, but also help her make sense of her feelings and understand how her mental and physical states were related.

After six months of being treated by this acupuncturist, Mona felt almost normal again. Because she had depleted her financial resources for the treatments, she discontinued the therapy. Even though these therapies had alleviated her symptoms better than any other had, once again the pain started creeping back a few months later.

In the meantime, Mona continued working at a stressful position and tried to live with it for a period of time. She once again became exhausted and tense. At thirty years of age, she felt it must be normal not to have the strength she once had. The extreme muscle tension she carried in her neck and shoulders seemed to get worse when her bladder pain flared, or vice-versa. She also thought she was developing repetitive-motion syndrome in her right hand. Mona felt her life was a disaster!

A few months later Mona moved to another city and state. She assumed that since she would not be working for awhile, things would get better. After a few days of intensive cleaning in her house, however, she was very sore, stiff, and experiencing lower back spasms. The next three days she spent in bed, barely able to move.

When Mona could walk again, she went to see a chiropractor she had selected from an ad which claimed a gentle, holistic, and emotion-sensitive approach. Even so, Mona was so skeptical and wary that under her breath she was daring the doctor to help her!

Nell Rodgers D.C. of Atlanta, Georgia, is a Certified NET Practitioner and Registered Psychiatric Nurse. She was kind, gentle, and engendered Mona's trust. Shortly after the initial treatment, once her condition was no longer critical, they embarked on a journey that Dr. Rodgers claimed would help do what had never been done before... get to and clear the underlying cause of her problem. Mona was not even sure what she meant. Dr. Rodgers explained that there were techniques that allowed her to unearth and heal subconscious emotional traumas, the very kind that she was certain were manifesting themselves as Mona's elusive illnesses.

The first large discovery they made through the NET process was of a memory from a severely traumatic moment that occurred over a decade earlier. The event had been a traumatic and profound loss of a loved one.

Having felt she was paralyzed and could do nothing about the loss, she was imprinted with "paralyzed will" in the bladder organ meridian point. What was most stunning was Mona's realization

that she had not thought of this moment even once since the time it had happened.

Dr. Rodgers cleared the NEC "paralyzed will" in the bladder meridian, and Mona burst into tears. She cried in a way she had not been able to do in years. Although she felt the pain of this memory all over again, she reports:

> ***"I felt it dissolving, like a massive dark cloud that just evaporated before my eyes, lifting a great weight off me!"***

Mona describes what so many others experience when an NEC is cleared or neutralized. For the next three months, countless memories both large and small, have dissipated. She then reports:

> ***"In ways I can hardly describe, I AM A NEW PERSON!"***

Dr. Rodgers used NEAT to relieve the emotional tension that was creating, both back problems and arm pain, as well. In just two weeks, she uncovered the cause of Mona's bladder pain. It was emotional in origin and a resulting metabolic malfunction was creating a burning sensation upon urination. After living with intense pain for over four years, not only did Mona get relief from the pain, she finally discovered there was nothing *wrong* with her bladder!

Several other NECs of "miffed," "bad memory," and "dread" were discovered. These had been imprinted when she was one, three, and four years old. Dr. Rodgers quickly cleared these NECs. Gradually, throughout her work with Dr. Rodgers, Mona blossomed physically, emotionally, spiritually, and intellectually. Each time she left Dr. Rodgers' office, she felt a profound change had taken place. She was seeing the world through different eyes. Whereas she once was resigned to the inevitable onslaught of old age at thirty years, she came to feel the same youthful enthusiasm and physical well-being that she had experienced as a child. Mona reported she felt as if layers of bitterness and cynicism had just melted away!

Another interesting aspect of Mona's case was that she had done this work in the absence and knowledge of any of the important people in her life, yet her relationships with them changed! The most profound effect was the change in her feelings toward her father. While previously she had been angry with her father and had avoided him for years, very literally she could hardly remember why she had been so angry!

Mona reports she actually began calling him just to chat, which was something she had never been able to do or even wanted to do. She became calm and confident as never before and came to feel newfound love both for herself and for all of life. Mona later related the following:

> *"They say the most debilitating fear is the fear of the unknown, and it's true. A large part of why NEAT seems so powerful to me is that it shows you that you do know, that actually your body knows what it needs even more than the most highly trained scientist does. Unlike in my experience with my family physician and even acupuncturists. I came to understand my body and the nature of what had gone wrong with a thoroughness that words could not match. I learned to FEEL the difference between right and wrong (in the body), to trust and love my body in a way I never knew possible."*

In reference to Mona's beautlful testimony, Dr. Scott Walker has said in his *TWENTY NEAT PREMISES*:

> *"It is healthy to become more conscious. Consciously and/or unconsciously, we are constantly creating our own life's circumstances for better or worse. Emotions, thoughts affect the Central Nervous System for better or worse."*

The following case is another example like Mona's in which the experience of grief fixated in the body, causing physical aberrations.

LISA

Lisa's father had recently died of cancer. Her family was a closely-knit, loving family. She was deeply grieved by her loss and sought relief for her loss through NEAT.

Her NECs were imprints from losses experienced long ago. Many NECs of "grief" were in the lung organ meridian access points, dating back to the age of three. She felt she had been replaced by her younger brother at the time of his birth. Her gall bladder/liver meridian access points held NECs of "anger" and "resentment" at the age of eight when she was treated cruelly by classmates who were resentful of her high intelligence and scholastic success.

The uterus meridian held "deserted" and "abandoned" NECs from when she was sixteen years old, and her boyfriend had mistreated her. The kidney meridian points were imprinted with "fear" and "paralyzed will" at the age of nineteen, at which time she was date raped in college. There were additional NECs surrounding the date rape of "anger" in the liver/gall bladder meridians, "lost" and "vulnerable" in the uterus meridians, "low self-esteem" in the pancreas meridian, and "disgust" in the stomach meridian. A Vanishing Twin was also discovered with the emotions of "grief" and "crying" in the right lung meridian access point.

These multiple old emotions, although not specifically "grief" in the lung meridians, were all related to loss of some kind. They were then triggered by her deeply experienced loss of her father some months earlier.

As the NECs were cleared one by one, the deepest pains of her loss were abated. With the old griefs cleared, she then became more in touch with her own resourceful, creative self. She began writing extraordinary poetry.

It is not that she no longer grieves her loss, but the charge on the loss has been greatly diminished. It is now channeled through the creative and esthetic expression in poetry, relationships, career, spiritual journey, and life in totality.

The following is one such writing. It exemplifies the expression of one who has suffered deep loss and, through her processing, has channeled one of her many gifts in this way.

> ***"Despite the alternate care,***
> ***Positive thinking and prayers,***
> ***My father paid the fare***
> ***To cross that bright river.***
> ***He sailed into the Light***
> ***On that May night***
> ***That we all did share,***
> ***Mother, brother,***

Sister, aunt.
We all were there
Ringed 'bout the bed
Watching each weak intake of air.
Holding vigil as he slipped freed
From battle with that silent monster,
Freed from pain from need to muster
Up the courage to continue
And saw him smile
His eyes alight
As he sailed forth
Into the Light."

April 30, 1995
~ Lisa

As I began writing this book in Taos, New Mexico, Lisa was there to run in a marathon. Afterwards, she came by for a visit. With a puzzled voice, she asked that I measure her height. "Whatever for? We know your height," I said. She simply reiterated her request.

I agreed, measured her, and was astonished to find that she was more than an inch taller! Thinking I had made a mistake, I measured her again, only to validate the original measurement. It was then that Lisa explained how the officials at the marathon had

measured everyone for their category of competition. She had protested the height they had measured her was incorrect.

Lisa was not a growing girl. She was thirty-four years old. It began to dawn on me that both her father and Lisa suffered severe scoliosis, a curvature of the spine (usually an "S" formation).

I inspected her spine, and instead of the "S" there was a perfectly straight spine, with the exception of the thoracic disc 12 (T12) still slightly slipped (D.C.'s call this subluxated).

This is one example among many that a subluxation in the spine can correct itself by the discharging of the emotional component creating it. Often when an NEC is cleared, a corresponding vertebra will quite naturally correct itself into alignment.

* * * * * * * * * * *

JANE

Jane was another patient of Dr. Nell Rodgers. She had bent over, causing something to snap in her back. This caused acute pain, extreme posture lean, and it was difficult for her to get up and down from a chair.

Before Dr. Rodgers could adjust her, she discovered it was necessary to clear an NEC to relieve the muscle tensions to allow the adjustment to be done. It turned out the NEC was "grief" in the right lung meridian access point.

Jane's current situation was precipitated by the unresolved grief of her son's suicide the previous November. Dr. Rogers tracked the pattern back to age five when the patient's father died. Her emotional reality at that age was that her father had left her. The visible grief was almost overwhelming to observe, Dr. Rodgers reports. Jane's deep, traumatic emotions were being expressed and released with wracking sobs which commenced the moment the "snapshot" memory of her father's death was brought to her conscious awareness.

A second NEC was discovered as Dr. Rodgers looked for the core issue surrounding the lower back pain. It was fixated at age seventeen, located in the spleen meridian as "lack of control over events."

Jane had been groomed for college by her family and at school all her life. She had always dreamed and planned for that goal. When she graduated from high school, however, her mother suddenly changed her mind and said, "No way! You will not go to college!"

With this shocking revelation and no explanation from her mother, Jane was devastated and expressed she "just wanted to die and go be with her father." However, Jane had not been able to control dying and going to be with her father. This emotion, of course, was repeated when she wanted to die and "go be with her son."

Dr. Rodgers discovered another NEC of "fear" in the right kidney meridian when post-testing, making the statement about being "ready, willing, and able to let go of pain."

> **(NOTE: This is one of the Personal Declarative {PD} statements the patient repeats in post-testing to determine if there are other NECs in the presenting problem.)**

Through this statement it was discovered that Jane, at the age of five, had touched her father's cold, dead body and interpreted that sensation as having done something wrong and in some way she had "caused" her father's death. The current precipitant of the pattern was that she had not been the quality mother, nor the good mother, nor done the right thing as a mother. She was, therefore, somehow, some way, to blame for her son's suicide.

In Jane's case, we see the importance of recognizing how her system recorded and processed these events. Her emotional realities were not necessarily historical realities! We know, for example, that because she *touched* her father's cold body, she could not have caused his death. Additionally, she was probably a great mother, and no matter what she had done as a parent, nothing would have stopped her son from committing suicide.

After NET/NEAT treatment Jane's back pain disappeared. She immediately stood erect, moved about effortlessly, and continues to do very well... free of back pain.

* * * * * * * * * * *

SONDRA

Often, doctors will take their spouses, children, or assistants to the NET/NEAT training so that they will better know and understand the process. They can experience it themselves firsthand and therefore better assist in the NET/NEAT treatment. The following case comes from one doctor's assistant.

Both Sondra and her husband had come from alcoholic families. The two of them had spent many hours in emotional release therapy so that they could function as a healthy family.

In 1981, their first child died at birth. In 1989, they lost another child, a son, in a motorcycle go-cart accident. Kendal, the child killed in this second tragic accident, had been very close to his older brother, Dave. They were often thought of as being twins because they were always together. Dave had always looked after his younger brother, Kendal.

When Kendal died, Dave blamed himself because he thought if he had been home, he could have prevented the accident and therefore could have prevented his brother's death.

Dave never shed a tear over Kendal's death. He refused to talk to anyone about it. He was not much of a verbal communicator and preferred to keep things to himself. His mother insisted he go to therapists for awhile but Dave, a proud adolescent, refused to cooperate. He reported that all the therapists he'd seen only wanted him to talk about his feelings. That was not his style, he said.

Dave developed a personality change over time, becoming extremely angry, accompanied by his body shaking uncontrollably. His parents bought a punching bag so he could beat on it to release some of the emotions. This effort was beneficial, but his mother knew something more was needed for Dave to find internal peace.

Sondra went to work for Dr. Kinkead, who was a trained NET/NEAT doctor. He encouraged Dave to be treated with NET/NEAT because he would not have to talk about his feelings. He explained all Dave would have to do is think about something that would upset him or re-experience his feelings about a distressful situation.

Sondra was a professionally trained psychotherapist and for twelve years previously had helped many. Dave refused her request to try NET/NEAT with Dr. Kinkead. He said if she could help him

he might do it, but otherwise no way! As she attempted to explain to Dave that she couldn't help him with psychotherapy because she was too close to him, his response was "Too bad. So sad."

Later, Sondra had the opportunity to attend a NEAT seminar as Dr. Kinkead's assistant. After returning home, the next time Dave became really upset, she offered to utilize the NEAT with him, to which he readily agreed.

Sondra discovered the original NEC was an event during the first trimester when Sondra was pregnant with Dave. The NEC was "sadness" located in the lung meridian access point. Sondra had suffered a miscarriage just prior to becoming pregnant with Dave. This fact was unknown to Dave's conscious mind. During the first trimester of the pregnancy with Dave, Sondra had been very fearful of also losing this baby (Dave).

> **(NOTE: NET/NEAT can detect information, at least the emotional reality, even pre-verbally, all the way back to the moment of conception as it is tapping into the storehouse and "diskettes" of information from the body system. More will be discussed later on this paradigm.)**

When the muscle testing revealed the NEC was recorded in the first trimester, Dave was dumbfounded. How was he to know what had happened or what he thought or felt at that time?! When Sondra suggested he think about not being wanted by her, he

laughed and replied, "Give me a break, Mom! You always wanted us. You are sometimes too good of a Mom. Sometimes I would like a little more freedom, in fact! Look how you acted when Kendal died!"

It was only then that Sondra shared with her son for the first time she had miscarried a baby just prior to getting pregnant with him. She also shared that she had suffered a deep paralyzing fear about facing the possibility of losing yet another baby!

Dave was a stout, strong football player and very difficult for Sondra to muscle test. When she finally convinced him to think about not being wanted, he became so weak that he could barely hold up his arm for testing. They discovered the emotion of "anguish" was fixated in the left lung during the first trimester. Sondra cleared it.

After the NET process, Dave's strength returned when asked to think about the anguish he felt by his Mom and his two brother's deaths. Dave was relieved and amazed that the process was so painless and he had not needed to talk it out with a therapist.

Sondra reports she and Dave now work with NET quite frequently. He continues to not be very verbally communicative. He adds he probably never will be because of his basically shy personality. He reports he always feels better after the NET treatment and that the grief, anguish, abandonment and anger issues are resolved. Sondra adds:

"It is good to have an emotional release therapy to help people who cannot or who do not wish to communicate verbally their innermost feelings with others."

This is an excellent type of therapy for teenagers as they tend not to feel any judgments because no one is prodding them about what they are thinking or feeling. The adolescent years, though seemingly not, are very sensitive and delicate years in which one is in transition between childhood and adulthood.

Partially still feeling like a child, partially feeling like the adult, yet knowing that neither is the absolute truth, the adolescent is in search of his/her own identity. The "who am I?" is exhibited in behaviors with which we, as parents and educators, are all too familiar. The emotions are bouncing off the wall, hormones are flying everywhere, and in the midst of this confusion, the ability to participate in a process in which one does not have to verbally express and reap benefit is indeed a gift!

NET/NEAT is therefore an excellent treatment for teenagers because it is non-threatening and no one is prodding them to verbally express or talk out their feelings. Most teenagers are fascinated, as was Dave, and often report they think NET/NEAT is fun!

* * * * * * * * *

In the following case we observe unresolved grief fixating in the body, creating allergic reactions.

*　*　*　*　*　*　*　*　*

PAT

In Clayton, Missouri, a thirty-seven year old single female named Pat was treated by Dr. Martin Paul Orimenko for problems relating to cat allergies. Pat reported that her reactions had been present since childhood. She had not experienced much relief from any anti-allergen medications or forms of therapy.

This particular allergy was presenting a most formidable problem for Pat, as she was engaged to the man of her dreams who had two cats that he adored! In the presence of his cats, Pat experienced the allergic reaction of uncontrollable sneezing. She expressed her concerns to Dr. Orimenko and requested her desired outcome of "I want *no* allergic reactions to cats!"

Dr. Orimenko began the NEAT process with this patient and located an NEC stored in the kidney meridian access point. This emotion was a "bad memory" regarding the grief of losing a friend. He then traced the NEC back to the age of eight years old. It was then that Pat recalled watching her pet kittty being run over by a car and killed right before her eyes!

Dr. Orimenko cleared the NEC and post-tested for grief regarding the lost pet. The emotion of "grief" was stored in the

lung meridian. In post-testing, Pat was then able to maintain a strong arm in repeating these statements:

"OK with the death of my kitty."

"OK with the loss of my friend."

"OK hearing about people losing their pets and loved ones."

"OK and safe with my fiance's cats."

The immediate reactions Pat experienced was no more sneezing around the cats! The most extraordinary results, however, have been the long-term ones. Pat now has two cats of her own! She reports and exhibits no allergic reactions to them!

Unresolved emotions such as "grief" can hold us back, blocking us from love, and in ways in which we may never dream. Our potential is there waiting for us to maximize ourselves by removing the blocks in our systems. If these blocks are not detected and cleared, they will create imbalance and eventually disease.

* * * * * * * * *

TOM

Tom, a thirty-two year old male, had been treated for severe neck pain on an ongoing basis by Dr. Timothy Campbell of Sherman Oaks, California. Tom had tried everything. He had seen medical doctors, learned and utilized meditation, had done energy work and many other traditional therapies...all without relief.

During one office visit, Dr. Campbell located the emotion of "grief" in both lung meridian access points. This emotion was imprinted when Tom was four months in-utero. At that time Tom's parents had been in an automobile accident. His father was driving and his mother was in the front passenger seat.

During the accident Tom's mother experienced deep grief that something really bad had happened to the baby she was carrying. The following five months, grieving for her unborn child, she fretted and worried. As hard as everyone tried to reassure her that the baby was fine, she imagined, as most pregnant mothers would, every horrible possibility that the accident had created for her baby.

Tom had been imprinted with his mother's "grief" that something bad had happened to him. Here is another example of the *Emotional Reality* and the *Historical Reality* being diverse, not being one and the same. Her Emotional Reality was that the accident created damage to her unborn child. The resulting "pre-grieving" is countered with the Historical Reality of a healthy baby, Tom, being born five months later.

Tom was astonished at this revelation, having no information or history related to him of this event. He was so eager to do some detective work on his own about this event.

Later, without divulging the NEAT experience with Dr. Campbell, Tom asked his mother about her pregnancy with him and if there had been any difficulties. She reported:

> **"Oh yes, my dear! Your father and I were in an auto accident and while neither of us were injured seriously, I worried and grieved about you the duration of the pregnancy. It was only when I held you in my arms, counted all your fingers, saw with my own eyes that you were absolutely beautiful and perfect did I believe that you had not been terribly affected in some way by the accident!"**

Tom really felt great after the NEAT treatment and his neck remains pain free. He was still free of the neck pain six months later at the time of his reporting.

*** * * * * * * ***

In my office I have a doll called " The Rosie Doll." On the back of each hand is a metal piece. When held by two or more people who then hold hands, Rosie begins to sing "Ring Around the Roses, Pocket Full of Posies." If one person disconnects holding hands, Rosie stops singing. If they reconnect, again Rosie sings! This is an example of how energy flows and that demonstrates we are not islands unto ourselves.

This next case is another example of the effects of NET/NEAT in healing grief, our connection, and the effect we have upon one another.

*** * * * * * * * ***

FLORENCE

Dr. Glen Miller's receptionist had started working for him in 1994. She had been retired from Bell Telephone and had been successfully treated by him for hearing loss in her left ear. She had heard Dr. Miller talk about the NEAT, but had never experienced the transformational work personally. Florence had been mourning the loss of her thirty-eight year old son who had died from a ruptured brain stem aneurysm.

Dr. Miller had previously treated a patient who had years earlier passed blood and spotted heavily when she was pregnant. Thinking she had aborted the pregnancy during the bleeding, the woman reported, however, that she maintained the pregnancy and later delivered a beautiful daughter who suffers from the diagnosed condition termed Gilles de la Tourette's Syndrome. This syndrome is rare and of unknown cause. It includes lack of muscle coordination, involuntary and purposeless movements, tics, and incoherent speech, grunts, barks, and so forth.

When the doctor reported this case to Florence, she replied that she had had the same experience with the son who had just died.

Dr. Miller asked if she would like to do the NEAT process relating to her son. She answered positively and they proceeded.

In checking her, Dr. Miller discovered an NEC connected to the pregnancy of her son. Her arm went weak at the verbal mention of the fourth month of pregnancy. Flo affirmed that was when she bled heavily at that time and had thought she had suffered a spontaneous abortion or that something was wrong with the baby.

Dr. Miller proceeded, discovering Florence had been pregnant with twins and that one of the twins was a girl. This twin had been re-absorbed back into the endometrium. The emotion which Florence's system had stored in the spleen at that time was "despair." He cleared the NEC and then post-tested. The muscle was then strong when exploring thoroughly the fourth month of that pregnancy.

The next day Florence entered the office, reporting to Miller the most beautiful dream from the previous night. In her dream, a beautiful girl was surrounded and bathed in a white light. The dream spanned thirty-eight years (the exact age of her son). At the end of the dream the beautiful girl went away, stating she was happy and thankful for the time she had been given. Florence reported she felt overwhelming peace during and following the dream.

A week later Flo's close friend, Mary, returned home from visiting in Colorado. Florence had not shared with her friend her

recent experience with Dr. Miller. Mary related to Florence a dream she had the previous week. In her dream, Florence had a beautiful baby girl thirty-eight years earlier. Mary related how happy this baby was and the wonderful feeling she had felt during and after her dream about the baby and Florence!

Dr. Miller is very attuned to the Native American heritage. He closed this case report with the following statement, as though in benediction:

> **"The Indians have a saying they repeat when they go into a sacred sweat lodge. It is: *'We are all related'.*" Florence reports a feeling of deep peace regarding the loss of her son and feels she can now move on with her life."**

* * * * * * * * *

Often, the Neuro Emotional Complex will imprint as one apparent emotion while its origin is actually in another emotion. The following case exemplifies this interesting phenomenon as we see the patient experiencing the emotion of "grief." In actuality, the emotion stems from the NEC of "fear" about losing his parent's love.

* * * * * * * * *

AARON

Aaron was a seven-year old boy who had been diagnosed by a medical doctor with Attention Deficit Disorder (ADD). He had severe concentration and behavioral problems in school. His parents reported being at school constantly consulting with his teachers, counselor and principal. These sessions were regarding the problems Aaron was both having and creating in the classroom and on the playground with other children.

A strong recommendation was made that Aaron be placed on medication to calm him down! His parents were reluctant to do so, particularly at his young age. They sought the assistance of Dr. Timothy Campbell.

When Dr. Campbell examined Aaron with the NET process, he discovered an NEC of "fear" in both kidneys. This imprint dated back to the age of three when Aaron feared losing his parent's love when his baby brother was born. Although he experienced the emotion of "grief" (from feeling he had been replaced by this baby on whom everyone seemed to focus their attention) in actuality the NEC was "fear."

Another very interesting aspect and influence in this case was that Aaron's paternal grandfather had died when Aaron's father was three years old. Aaron's father had no male role model and had "grieved" and "feared" that he would not be a good father to

his own children. In addition to his own NEC, Aaron had also been sensitive to and imprinted with his father's NEC, which his father had experienced as a child.

After Dr. Campbell cleared the NEC (with some difficulty, as Aaron was so hyperactive), Aaron immediately calmed down. His mother later reported the teachers at school had called and inquired as to what they had done to calm Aaron down. They reported:

> **"Aaron is a totally different boy…is calm, can concentrate, is not a 'trouble maker,' is doing well academically, and is cooperative!"**

Although the emotion was imprinted as "fear," there was also the feeling of grief at being replaced and losing his parent's love.

*** * * * * * * * ***

In the *Course of Miracles* it is purported that love means letting go of fear. From my perspective, there are two basic emotions and all other human emotions fall under one or the other…love or fear.

To acknowledge and address our individual fears is a big step in our growth process. However, until they are resolved, released, or cleared, we will be at the mercy of the NEC.

Dr. Wayne Dyer, in his book *Everyday Wisdom*, considers negativity, imbalance, and judgement as the three ingredients that clog our souls. All three of these are based in fear.

Furthermore, Neal Walsch, in his book *Conversations With God*, considers thought to be very creative and powerful. If we think and feel fear, we will attract fear energy. According to Walsch, love is the *absolute* and the feeling of love is to experience God. And when we move into that absolute, we move into love. To release or to give up fear means that we are then open to experience love and who we really are, because love is all there really is.

This is the ultimate reality. That which *grows* us, molds us, as the potter does with the clay, into the creation that we truly are. *Love* transcends all...time, events, history. Love remains the one *absolute*.

The Neuro Emotional Anti-sabotage Technique can move us into a place of love by removing that which blocks us from that love. The following case is an example of the power of such love and courage.

* * * * * * * * *

KARL

Karl was a sixty-three year old male suffering from Parkinson's Disease (diagnosed in 1980), clinical depression, bladder incontinence, and cardiac disease. He and his wife Mattie had one son and two grandchildren.

Despite the doctor's insistence that there was no evidence NET/NEAT could help Karl, his sixty-five year old wife had insisted on flying him fifteen hundred miles to achieve hoped-for success to alleviate his debilitating state.

Upon arriving at their destination, exhausted from the journey, Mattie reported, "We have prayed for a miracle...and we've already received one...we made it here! If we get another one, that is wonderful dessert!" Obviously, Mattie and Karl were very devoted to one another!

Karl could not walk unassisted and had a severe and constant tremor. He was mentally dulled, mostly by his many prescriptive medications, and had difficulty following a course of thought in conversation. Physically he was very constrained. Mattie and Karl were desperate for help.

Mattie reported that he had been a successful salesman for IBM when his symptoms began some seventeen years earlier. In the beginning the Parkinson's had been mild. However, by the time he was fifty-four years old he was forced to retire.

Karl had participated in two different research studies in the years following his forced retirement. In one of the studies he was given a treatment that worked well and his symptoms abated. He couldn't, however, be given any more of the researched medications at the conclusion of the study because the FDA had not yet approved them for use. His urinary urgency had made him very nervous, forcing numerous trips to void the bladder during the night. Mattie was exhausted from years of interrupted sleep to assist him eight to ten times per night.

Karl and Mattie had sought treatment with a Naturopathic Doctor (ND) at one point. An ND is a doctor who treats illnesses using natural remedies, such as foods, herbs, homeopathies, vitamins, and so forth. He performed acupuncture on Karl. The ND discovered his adrenal glands were not functioning properly.

Karl was taking the traditional Parkinson's Disease medications, anti-depressants and several cardiac medications. In total, he was taking eight prescribed medications several times per day. His mental and emotional affect was very dulled.

Mattie, exhausted from the long trip, was unable to get him to the doctor's office for NET/NEAT intervention, so the doctor went to their motel room. When she first saw him, knowing how far they had traveled, her heart sank. His Parkinson tremor was so severe she wondered if she would even be able to muscle test him.

After taking his history and briefly educating them on the technique, and with a prayer in her heart, she proceeded. She trusted that something positive must come from their encounter.

It took both Mattie and the doctor to physically move him from a soft chair to a straight back chair so that she could work with him. Most of his history was completed with Mattie providing the information. Karl was so mentally slow from all the medications that it was difficult to retrieve the information. Once accomplished, and with his breathless insistence, they proceeded with the process.

Realizing she had only a very short time to work with Karl, the doctor checked his muscle strength on several statements. Surprisingly, in spite of the severe tremors, he had strong muscles.

Wanting to get right to the core issues, she asked Karl to repeat the statement, "I'm Okay with having Parkinson's Disease." His arm went weak, dropping like a limp rag.

> **(NOTE: Remember that "Okay" means generally neutral and not a preference.)**

The doctor then began the investigation into his history. Muscle testing revealed he held an emotional reality that he had been a triplet in-utero. There were three male fetuses, two of whom did not survive. The time of Karl's NEC imprint was in the first trimester. Karl confirmed he had been told that his mother almost had a miscarriage at that time.

The emotion was "low self-esteem" located in the pancreas and spleen meridian access points. The "low self-esteem" he felt was due to feeling that he could not save his brothers and that something must "be wrong" with him that they left him.

Karl began to cry as he related that was exactly how he had felt with his first wife...as if he could never do anything right. The doctor also discovered one of the triplets had *re-absorbed* in-utero into Karl's cranial/head area, and the other triplet into the endometrium! The doctor moved quickly to clear these NECs as Karl's energy was dissipating quickly under the emotional strain.

While hoping for the best, the doctor was not prepared for what happened next. Suddenly, Karl, who just minutes earlier had struggled with the help of two females to move only inches into a straight back chair, jumped up unassisted out of the chair! He began rapidly pacing around the room exclaiming:

> ***"I don't know what just happened, but something wonderful! I don't know what has happened, but 'THANK GOD'!"***

Mattie began to sob as she exlaimed, "He's not been like this for years! I have my Karl back! Look at his eyes! They are clear and alive!"

And indeed they were. There was not a dry eye in the room!

The next morning after the initial NEAT treatment, Mattie awakened alarmed. She feared something dreadful had happened to Karl as she realized he had not called out for her assistance to the bathroom during the night. She was astonished to see him sitting on the side of his bed, fully dressed and reporting he had only needed to make one trip all night and had managed quite well on his own steam!

For the remainder of the week they were in Texas, Karl never let Mattie out of his sight. He went everywhere with her...to the grocery store, to the Mall, and even to Palo Duro Canyon, a smaller version of the Grand Canyon, where they hiked as they had loved to do years earlier. As the week progressed they had a wonderful and beautiful time together in a way they had not been able to in years!

The most amazing symptom change, however, was his loss of the typical Parkinson tremor! His posture was more upright and he walked without even the shuffle, a typical gait of the Parkinson Disease patient. The doctor was amazed, astounded and as grateful as Karl and Mattie were.

In Karl and Mattie's courage to travel so far with his severe physical impairments, they were void of fear. Their hope, faith and love created the energy and possibility for his healing with NEAT.

I am reminded of and offer the following as an ode to you and your shared love, Mattie and Karl:

"There is beauty in the forest
When the trees are green and fair,
There is beauty in the meadow
When wild flowers scent the air.
There is beauty in the sunlight
And the soft blue beams above.
Oh, the world is full of beauty
When the heart is full of love."

Author Unknown

* * * * * * * * *

In the next chapter, I will explore the subject of mental/emotional health. The impact NET/NEAT has had on the individuals' lives is profound.

CHAPTER FIVE

NET/NEAT HEALING EMOTIONAL ILLNESS

"Sometimes how I react to what happens is more important than what actually happens."
Michael Grinder

In thc *Chinese People's Daily* newspaper, a column on "*Human Rights in the United States*" was published. As an introduction to this chapter, a portion from that column is quoted here as food for thought on the subject of emotional health in the United States.

"In 1990, for every 100,000 Americans incarcerated there were 455 Chinese locked up in jail. This allowed the United States to remain the 'World Champion' with an incarceration rate one third higher than the next runner-up, South America."

If this is true reporting, is this a statement or an indictment about the status of our culture's emotional health?

Dr. Walker is very clear that NET and NEAT are about *physiology*, not *psychology*. He states:

> ***"NET concerns itself with the aberrant physiology of the autonomic system present in the Neuro Emotional Complex. The ramifications of these effects spill over into the motor system, causing weakened muscles, persistent subluxations, and so forth. NET is an intervention into the autonomic system."***

It is obvious that the body is a whole. Dr. Walker encourages referrals to psychologists or psychotherapists and others in the behavioral professions who also understand that the body heals itself. He insists that the NET doctor and the psychotherapist can provide a very complementary role for their patients' improvement as they work in tandem. Profound examples are recorded in the following case reports.

*** * * * * * * * ***

Dr. Khelly Webb, a trained NET doctor from Los Alamitos, California, reports she had the opportunity to meet and introduce NET/NEAT to Clinton Turrell, CEO, President of the Breakthrough Foundation. The Breakthrough Foundation works with hard core kids, gangs and adolescents who are in serious trouble and considered "Youth at Risk."

The Breakthrough Foundation takes the youths who are on the edge, those whose strong prognosis is winding up dead or in a prison system. The BTF strives to teach these youths the techniques that will assist them in taking control of their lives and thereby getting an education, a job, elevating themselves, and at attaining a better quality of life.

Dr. Webb's introduction of NET/NEAT to Mr. Turrell eventually led her to travel to a detention center in Arizona. Mr. Turrell had recognized the impact and possibilities NET/NEAT could have for the troubled adolescents and strongly encouraged Dr. Webb to go to the Arizona Project to work as a consultant with the staff.

The Arizona Project was made up of the Breakthrough Foundation and the Youth-At-Risk Programs. Most of these youths have higher than normal intelligence. Eighty percent of them had seen a friend killed in the previous six months. Most were alcohol and drug abusers. Most sincerely believed they would be dead by the age of twenty-one. All of them believed they would not live past thirty years of age!

Initially, Dr. Webb was to be a member of the medical staff's Well Being Team, only to determine whether or not NEAT would be helpful with the youths. On her first day an emergency situation arose when one of the youths became suicidal. Therapists, psychologists, and social workers had been working with him unsuccessfully.

Dr. Webb was asked to intervene. She addressed the situation then offered the NEAT with this young man. She proceeded, with their encouragement. Within approximately twenty minutes of the technique he was a transformed young man and a happy sixteen-year old youth!

Dr. Webb related to the staff that either this was a miracle or the kid was faking. She strongly recommended they observe him closely. She later reported:

"As it turned out, we had a miracle."

The youth's sponsor who lived in Phoenix was so impressed with the positive changes in the young man's voice over the phone that he drove some fifty miles to find out what Dr. Webb had done. The sponsor confirmed the definite positive change.

At that point, Dr. Webb was shifted from observer to active participant and began working with the entire staff of psychologists, psychotherapists, social workers and psychiatrists.

* * * * * * * * *

JIMMY

At the Arizona Project, one of the sixteen year old boys was beginning to go into a paranoid schizophrenic state. Three

psychologists had been working with him for eighteen hours in an attempt to prevent his going into that total breakdown. Again, Dr. Webb was asked to see what the NEAT could do for this youth. The psychologists needed a cause or a source point for the breakdown in order to work with him. Thus far they had been unsuccessful in achieving that goal.

Dr. Webb was escorted into the room where she was to work with Jimmy. Seven guards encircled them. Jimmy looked much younger than his chronological years. He was very overweight and had poor eyesight. A portion of his history included his observing a friend commit suicide by jumping off a cliff. Jimmy had been thirteen then.

Jimmy did not want to be tested. He thrashed around and was very agitated. Dr. Webb worked patiently to establish rapport with this young man and to gain some sense of safety and trust. Once she accomplished this, it took approximately five minutes to get to the core problem.

Dr. Webb discovered that when he was a three-year old boy he had been violently gang-raped by six men who were all trusted family members! The NECs of "lost" and "vulnerable" in the prostate organ meridian access point were treated and cleared.

Another NEC of "paralyzed will" in the right kidney meridian, imprinted also at that time, was treated and cleared. There were

other NECs of "grief" in the right lung meridian point and "anger" in the liver meridian point. Dr. Webb cleared them all.

As a result of Dr. Webb's treatment of this troubled young man they were then able to set up a treatment plan with a psychologist who specialized in male sexual trauma. The psychotherapist reported he would never have been able to reach that depth had NEAT not been used. Because of Dr. Webb's intervention, this young man was prevented from going into what could have been a permanent psychotic state.

* * * * * * * * *

JEFF

Jeff, another youth at risk at the Project, had run away from the program. He had attempted suicide six times. Through quick medical attention he was returned to life, very agitated. Dr. Webb was asked to see this young man with the task of finding a source cause for his aberrant behavior.

Using NEAT, she discovered that the issue was not what had originally been thought by Jeff and the psychotherapists. Previously, Jeff had verbally expressed anger and frustration toward his stepfather as he had felt betrayed by him.

Dr. Webb discovered instead, that Jeff actually had an NEC concerning his mother. He held an NEC of "deserted" in the heart

meridian. She had married the stepfather when Jeff was much younger. At that time he had felt deserted by her. Jeff had expressed that he loved his mother and feeling "deserted" by her was not an acceptable emotion for him to feel. According to his own inner value system (his reality), therefore, the problem was with his stepfather.

Dr. Webb cleared the NEC and Jeff then worked with the psychologists and psychotherapists from this different perspective. He later was dismissed from the program and returned to school where he was reported doing very well socially and academically.

Dr. Webb reports:

> **"The psychotherapists were so impressed with these cases that they wanted to have their own sessions of NET/NEAT to find out what was going on with themselves and to clear their own issues."**

As a result of her work at the Arizona Project, Dr. Webb was hired by the members of the Break Through Foundation at their national headquarters in San Francisco. She has also met with the members of other similar organizations doing the NET/NEAT with the board members from other parts of the country. After initially working with them, she now refers them to their local NET Success graduates.

Dr. Webb continues with her passionate beliefs about NET and NEAT by saying:

> **"I personally believe that NET and NEAT are the most important tools that we have, either in the chiropractic or in the psychology fields, to help people who are on the edge...those who are at high risk and who have already been through all the other kinds of programs and are still stuck. This is an opportunity to break through."**

Dr. Webb describes the working environment at the Project as not being the easiest of her professional life. Seven guards were always posted in the room for security as she worked with each youth. However, she quickly adds, her overall experience was extremely rewarding. In using the NET/NEAT she observed the kids beginning to assume responsibility for themselves, both in behavior and attitude. At one point she overheard two youths who were engaged in an argument. One stepped back and then said to the other:

"Hey! You need to get 'NET-ed'!!"

With this statement as a testimonial, she believed they had really understood the grasp and power of NEAT. These troubled young men were so impressed with the rapid relief and changes within

themselves that they were eager to experience more! Often they would refer to their wanting to experience the technique with:

"Hey! Anybody wanna play?"

The following story is another illustration of the value of NET and NEAT in mental/emotional health issues.

*** * * * * * * * ***

LUCILLE

When Lucille entered the doctor's office her affect was obviously depressed. Her speech was slow, her posture slumped and she looked as though she could start crying at any moment. She began by stating slowly that she did not know where to begin. Eighteen months previously, she reported that she could not have even come into the office nor spoken about her feelings.

Lucille had been retired from teaching school after serving thirty years. She and her husband planned many fun adventures for their remaining years. Following years of poor health, however, her husband had died three years prior to her office visit. He had suffered tuberculosis, cancer, and many surgeries.

Lucille had one son who had been very close to his father and had deeply grieved his father's death. He was a grown man and was very independent. Finishing his PhD in a distant state, he was soon to marry a wonderful girl.

As a young woman, Lucille's family had not initially accepted or approved of her new husband. Eventually, however, they had come to love and accept him.

It was learned that Lucille's father had died suddenly when she was sixteen years old. Her mother was never happy, was not emotionally available to anyone, and nagged her father on a consistent basis. She went to live with her maternal grandparents during her high school years. While that was a nurturing environment, she missed her family of origin.

Lucille had one younger sibling, a sister whom she described as the "cute one with the great personality that everyone loved." She had always felt inferior to her younger sister. At the same time she deeply admired all the wonderful qualities that she felt she did not possess herself.

Months earlier, Lucille had been placed on an anti-depressant medication by her physician. He told her it was his impression she had suffered a "breakdown." During that time she retreated from everyone, was afraid to drive, unable to converse with people. It was then that she realized she had been depressed most all her life.

The most pressing recent event was that her sister had alienated herself from Lucille and had shut her out of her life. Because of her sister's popularity and influence with the extended family members, they also seemed to shut her out. Family had always been very important to Lucille and this familial exclusion had been

very painful for her. Her sister no longer included her in family gatherings. In one incident, she had condemned Lucille for everything she had ever done wrong in the past thirty-nine years. This was followed by her sister telling Lucille that she never wanted her in her life again!

Obviously in deep pain from reporting this event, Lucille began sobbing uncontrollably. Alone and miserable, this wonderful human being who had served hundreds of children as an excellent educator, stated that she just wanted "out of my body" (death). Due to religious beliefs, however, suicide was out of the question.

The doctor recommended NEAT to Lucille, explaining its basis briefly. Though not understanding the technique, she weakly replied affirmatively with, "I'll try anything."

The doctor proceeded with the process, finding the first NEC imbedded in the stomach meridian access point with the emotion of "disgust," imprinted at the age of three. It was her mother's "disgust" with life, especially with her own life. Lucille's system had processed this emotion with a belief that she was not good enough for a happy life. She took on this emotion during an incident in which she overheard her parents arguing.

This NEC was cleared and then immediately another NEC of "grief" was discovered in the left lung meridian access point. This NEC was imprinted soon after her younger sister's birth. She reported how she had felt replaced, ugly, and insignificant in light

of her sister's beauty. Lucille remembered all the attention showered upon the new baby and Lucille began to cry again.

As the doctor cleared this latest NEC Lucille immediately ceased crying and reported a feeling of "flowing, melting, and feeling really good."

Her facial expression noticeably changed as she smiled, her posture straightened, and her breathing became much deeper. In the following months, she continued with the NEAT sessions. Many NECs were discovered and cleared from the lung meridians on "grief," "sadness," and "crying."

During this period, Lucille suffered more lung infections and bronchitis. Most of her NECs, imprinted at very early ages, were triggered by the combination of her husband's death, her son's reaching adulthood (out of the nest), and her sister's perceived total rejection of her.

While most of her NECs were located in the lung meridian access points, many were also imprinted in the uterus meridian with "lost" and "vulnerable." With all the losses, the grief and sadness had left her, as she stated, "yes, I really felt 'lost' and 'vulnerable'."

Two years later Lucille reported that after a long period of no contact with her sister, she had built a new life for herself. She had released her sister and her dreams of ever having a renewed relationship.

She happily reported, however, that after three years of no contact, her sister had recently invited Lucille to her fiftieth wedding anniversary party. She had also come to Lucille's house several times and had spoken with her on the phone in a congenial manner.

Extended family members also responded positively to Lucille and included her in family gatherings, travel, and communication. She now enjoys higher energy, traveling, visiting with family, excellent health and is very active in the community, church, and is a nursing home volunteer. Lucille reports:

> **"I never thought I could do it. I feel good about myself for the first time in my life, and I am a happy person. It feels so good to reclaim my life!"**

Lucille, now busy with volunteer work, cooking and baking for friends, family and nursing home, is traveling and enjoying the love of her family. Most importantly, the debilitating clinical depression is gone and she no longer needs the antidepressant medication.

Not all is perfect with her sister as of yet, but the important aspect of this work is that Lucille is no longer charged in the same way with her sister's behavior of exclusion. The pain level, therefore, is greatly reduced when and if her sister chooses to exclude her from some family activities.

JOAN

Joan had experienced learning and emotional problems all her life. Her mother asked Dr. Glen Miller if NET/NEAT could help someone who was soon to be committed to a psychiatric hospital for the third year in a row. Joan had been committed the previous two years for three to six months each year for in-house treatment. Dr. Miller's response was, "The best I can do is to examine Joan and see."

The following week Joan sat in the waiting room staring at the corner. Dr. Miller guided her into the examining room where she found another corner in which to stare. Her mother reported that Joan was on five prescriptive anti-depressant drugs.

He attempted communication with Joan with little success. At this point he chose to use the mother as a surrogate tester.

> (NOTE: This is a technique in which another individual touching the patient is muscle tested when the patient is unable to be tested. The information gathered is correctly applicable to the patient as there is the energy connection (or circuitry) through the touch, much like the example of the Rosie Doll. This surrogate muscle is used by veterinarians to obtain from animals. Pediatric practitioners also use the surrogate muscle of an adult when they work with infants.

As Joan was not responding, he felt he had no other recourse and proceeded accordingly.

Dr. Miller touched Joan and asked the question, "Do you want to participate?" Joan did not understand. He further explained, "This is how we go about tapping into the subconscious." At this point she replied with a slight recognition with "oh." Knowing that she did not understand, he persisted with five more attempts. Finally he gained her participation and they were in the playing field, he reported.

Believing he had only a short time to get into Joan's Body/Mind System, he jumped directly to the area or subject of love. There he found NECs of "abandoned" located in the heart meridian. This emotion was imprinted when she was seven years old. Her father had drowned along with an uncle and two of her brothers.

Dr. Miller then traced even further back to the age of five. At that point Joan became very distant and withdrawn. The mother replied that this was a time Joan went to kindergarten and there was an incident in which Joan's father went into a rage.

At that time her father had not wanted Joan to go to school because he felt she was very slow mentally and had a learning problem. He believed she would be an embarrassment to him. His ego and name were in jeopardy. Joan's mother then interjected, "My husband was a real bitch about Joan going to school." As she made this statement, Dr. Miller felt the trembling within Joan begin.

He then asked Joan to make a mental picture of her being a five year old girl and especially when it had to do with her intelligence. Her appearance was one of terror and confusion as to what happened to her. The drugged and depressed mental state made it even more difficult for Joan to concentrate.

For the next fifteen minutes Dr. Miller continued to work with Joan in an attempt to get her to make a picture and feel the feeling surrounding that particular event and her father's rage.

(NOTE: In NEAT, it is necessary for the patient to have or visually hold the "snapshot" of the problem event before the doctor can make the adjustment.)

Eventually she reported she had a picture and he seized the moment, asking if she could see or feel how worthless she had felt in the eyes of her father at the age of five. She replied, "Yes".

Dr. Miller reported his hesitancy in requesting Joan to re-visit that event when she was already very emotionally weak, vulnerable, and scheduled for psychiatric hospitalization soon. He pushed ahead, however, finding a "low self-esteem" NEC in the spleen meridian and cleared it.

Next, Dr. Miller inwardly questioned the efficacy of the technique being utilized concurrently with psychotropically-drugged

individuals who are clinically diagnosed with psycho-pathology. With trepidation he post-checked Joan and found strong muscle tests in "surrounding the dragon," or best known as "post-testing" (testing to validate that changes have occurred).

(NOTE: In Chinese acupuncture there is a technique known as "Surrounding the Dragon." The "Dragon" is the focus of the pain and needles are inserted in key acupuncture points in the vicinity. In NEAT, the "Dragon" is the NEC. During the post-testing, following the release or discharge of the NEC, the doctor always makes sure the patient is emotionally congruent with all aspects of all avenues pertaining to the NEC that has weakened the system.)

Joan returned on a re-schedule date two days later. She cracked a slight smile and looked away quickly as Dr. Miller saw her in the waiting room. Once in the treatment room, however, she spoke slowly for the first time and said she felt a change. He re-checked the emotions previously cleared and found her system was still strong and congruent.

Dr. Miller continued by processing other NECs of "grief" in the lung meridians at the age of three at the time in which she felt rejected by her father, and these were cleared. A treatment plan was set up now that both the doctor and Joan's mother could see the noticeable improvement from only two sessions.

Joan's mother agreed to bring her in twice a week and each visit revealed more improvement. She had become more focused rather than staring out into space and her speech improved with each visit.

Dr. Miller noticed, however, that she continued to show a lack of emotional expression, especially that of "happiness." She could not say she was happy and maintain a strong muscle test, nor could she say "I love myself." When asked why, she replied, "I can only love other people." She continued, "That is just the way I am."

The NECs of "paralyzed will" in the right kidney M.A.P., "lost" and "vulnerable" in the thyroid meridian, and "bad memory" in the bladder meridian were discovered and discharged. These all had been imprinted at the age of six to eighteen months old. To Dr. Miller's amazement, Joan was able to make the post-testing statements (Surround the Dragon) successfully.

After three weeks, without encouragement from anyone, Joan began taking herself off the prescriptive drugs. Joan's continued progress was amazing. She smiled and verbalized her dreams and positive expectancies for her future. This was in sharp contrast to the Joan of three weeks earlier who had been so depressed, staring into space, non-responsive, and destined to psychiatric hospitalization possibly for the rest of her life.

In the past, Joan's husband and children had learned to use her for their own benefit. Now Joan was learning to reclaim her

power, her dignity, gain control of her own energy, and not give it away unless she chose to do so.

She had positively tested for NECs of emotional and physical abuses. These were "anger" and "resentment" in the gall bladder/liver meridians at the age of two. These were cleared and Dr. Miller reports that Joan continues to grow stronger emotionally, physically, mentally, and spiritually.

Three months later Joan's sister came into his office for treatment and astounded the doctor as she said:

"Thank you for giving me my sister back after twenty years!"

To which Miller added:

"Later, I welcomed Joan back into the human race. Her now wonderful laughter is music to my ears!"

In her book, *God Speaks to Me*, Eileen Caddy encourages humanity, as related to this case, to be more joyful and bring more laughter into our living.

This also appears to be the earnest plea of the patient in the following case as she in desperation seeks help from her physician.

*** * * * * * * ***

CHARLOTTE

Charlotte suffered from chronic depression most of her life. In the previous eight years her condition had become acute. She increasingly found it extremely difficult to perform normal daily functions. She reported having her spouse hold her as she sobbed almost daily in despair.

At her husband's insistence, she would repeat affirmation statements such as, "I have a good job." "I have a good career." "I have a good income." "I have a good relationship." "I know my husband loves me." When able to comply, she would end these statements wailing, "And I don't know what's wrong!" This went on for five years with only very brief interludes of absence from these episodes.

In the spring of 1995, her physician had treated her for adrenal stress and exhaustion. This paved the way to discharge NECs in the adrenal meridian. He added nutritional support to bring the adrenals back into recovery.

The NEC uncovered was imprinted at age three when her new-born sister was brought home from the hospital. The scene was one in which the father was holding the weeping mother, suffering from post-partum depression. The grandmother, holding the new-born, experienced anguish in not knowing what to do to help her weeping daughter. Charlotte, watching the four of them and sensitive to the

situation, was imprinted with her grandmother's emotion of "anguish."

A secondary emotion of the same event was Charlotte's "yearning" to be loved, which was held in the left lung meridian. This was imprinted at the time of her birth because her mother had never known how to hold, cuddle, or in any way convey love to Charlotte. As a result, Charlotte was bottle fed and not held during feeding time. Additionally, signifying her mother's obsessive-compulsive tendencies, her mother had written (inappropriately) in her baby book, "Charlotte is progressing well in her toilet training at the age of six months!"

Charlotte's depression lifted immediately following that session. On the next few visits she reported she was "afraid it was going to come back." However, six weeks later she remained symptom free. After years of deep depression and tears, Charlotte now continues to have total absence from that underlying melancholia, gloom, and doom.

CATERPILLAR...
COCOON....
BUTTERFLY...
CAN ONE NOT BELIEVE IN MIRACLES....?
Gwen Frostic

CHAPTER SIX

NEURO EMOTIOMAL TECHIQUE
LEARNING SKILLS AND EDUCATION

A mother of one of my patients, an educator, was a poet. The following poem is one she wrote in honor of her daughter and others who teach our children.

"For the teacher in each of us—
Time flies, but life goes on—
The rewards, the surprises,
The glitches
All mix and mingle—
Not as we ordain them
But as they react to the Universe
Yet may we never believe
That what we do doesn't matter—
What we do can strengthen or shatter,
Support or batter.
Thank God for persons like you
Who know the difference
And act upon it.

Jean

Learning difficulties in students continue to be a challenge for educators. Much has been discovered and utilized with those who are diagnosed as learning impaired and learning disabled. NET/NEAT has been successfully utilized in some very difficult cases. Dr. Khelly Webb reports the following case histories.

*** * * * * * * ***

LORI

Lori was a twenty-eight year old woman who had desperately wanted a college education to study art. However, since she had "flunked out" of high school, it looked as though her dream would never be realized.

As a student, she had been diagnosed with emotionally based learning problems. Lori was inherently an extraordinary artist. She loved the computer arts. She continued to take classes but kept failing. She was again told that she had emotionally based learning disabilities.

When Lori came to see Dr. Webb she explained how she would use a different process to determine the source of Lori's learning problems. Lori agreed "to play" as Dr. Webb endearingly refers to NEAT. NEAT revealed that when Lori was a very young girl she discovered that learning was a very dangerous process. Lori could barely add or spell.

At the age of five Lori had been ridiculed by other children when she risked herself in answering a teacher's question in kindergarten. The answer was incorrect, and to make matters worse, the teacher (it appeared to Lori) laughed at her response. The NEC of "bad memory" located in the kidney meridian was cleared.

Soon, Lori learned to type, spell, and even took calculus the last time Dr. Webb saw her. Lori received a scholarship to study art for six months in England. She successfully completed that course of study, and is, at the time of this reporting, preparing to leave for France to be a secretary for a sculptor where she can continue her pursuit and training as an artist! Dr. Webb observed that this was quite a dramatic change for a rather quiet, non-assertive girl!

* * * * * * * * *

As this case was reported, I wistfully thought of what NEAT could have accomplished with one of my own children.

When my oldest son was three years old he learned to read...not sophisticatedly, but satisfactorily for himself. It was his favorite pleasure. When we went anywhere, he only asked us to bring him back a book...not a truck, train, ball, or even candy. He could hardly wait until he was old enough to go to school.

When he was in kindergarten, first grade, and the first semester of second grade, he felt he was in heaven. He looked forward to

each day at school, disappointed on the days school was not in session.

During the middle of second grade, however, we were transferred and had to move to another city. It was not until near the end of that semester that we became aware of his teacher's cruel method of discipline. It was brought to our attention that the children who made a mistake in the reading circle were required to stand up on her desk. She then made the other children march around the desk and ridicule the child!

While Mark was an excellent reader and was never forced to stand upon her desk to be the brunt of the ridiculing, he *never loved to read again!* Every attempt to encourage and rekindle his joy in reading failed.

Always a very sensitive child, I know today that he was imprinted with the "anguish" of the other children who were ridiculed. This experience affected his entire academic career from that point forward. While he is now a successful young businessman, I wonder what might have been his path had he been treated with NEAT soon after that experience to discharge that traumatizing event!

I grew up "in the school yard." Both my parents were educators. My mother was a master elementary school teacher, dad was a secondary school educator, coach, principal, and then superintendent. All of my father's five siblings and their spouses

were educators, save one. I was learning, from a very young age, about the challenges of stimulating the learning process and blocks therein within students.

As I listen to educators today discuss the issues and challenges facing them daily in the classroom, I experience momentary exhaustion and frustration. I am amazed at the seemingly insurmountable tasks of educating students today. I marvel at their ability to meet the challenges they face each and every day. Dr. Wayne Dyer reminds us in his book *Everyday Wisdom*, however, that none of us knows enough to be pessimistic.

Therefore, the thought and hope of what NEAT could, can, and will do for countless students, educators, and parents brings me out of that negative thought-form.

The following case is another example of supporting this hope and dream as NEAT reverses negative learning experiences.

* * * * * * * * *

CATHERINE

Catherine had always wanted to become a building engineer but had severe problems with self-esteem about learning. She was in her late twenties, attending a training course in an attempt to fulfill her dreams.

Catherine was the only female in the program. The instructors were rude to her and discouraged her at every step in the training. She had great difficulty dealing with the criticism and confrontation.

A project was assigned in one of the classes. Her instructor told her that no female had ever graduated from the program and he would personally see to it that she never did! Frustrated and frightened of imminent failure, she sought assistance and treatment from Dr. Khelly Webb.

Utilizing NEAT with Catherine, Dr. Webb discovered she had an NEC imprinted from a childhood confrontation at age seven relating to a learning experience. The emotion was "paralyzed will" located in the right kidney meridian. This was imprinted at the age of five when she was unable to give the right answer to her kindergarten teacher in front of all the other children.

After the NEC was cleared, Catherine later happily reported that she had been given the highest score in the class on her project! Also, Catherine is now the head building engineer of three hospitals. She has become very appropriately assertive as the only female supervising an all-male team in her city!

* * * * * * * * *

Years ago I was completing a post graduate Education Psychology Fellowship at the University of Oklahoma. There were ten of us in the program serving as consultants for the State of

Oklahoma educational systems. Thousands of hours were spent testing students throughout the state for learning disabilities, emotional disabilities, and maturity development. We were interpreting, consulting, and making recommendations for the challenged students, programs, and educators. It was an excellent program, one for which I shall forever be grateful.

As we served in that capacity, we were rapidly made aware that all too often when students were not performing as expected, many expressed the belief that something was wrong with them.

Frequently during first grade little Johnny learns that something is wrong with him unless he makes a perfect score on his paper. Somehow he gets the message that he did not measure up, that he failed to do as well as he should have done. He feels ashamed because his well-intentioned parents told him to do his best. His best would be 100, not 90, 60, or 35.

From the beginning Johnny has learned that he has failed...and then that becomes a belief that he *is* a failure. The innate desire for exploring, experiencing, inquiring, and learning about himself in his world has now been dented. He has turned in another less constructive and less creative direction.

The following case again exemplifies the negative learning experience stored as an NEC and the damaging impact upon a life.

* * * * * * * * *

JAMES

When James entered the doctor's office, he could hardly fill out the registration form. He had been a construction worker and due to an injury was now on a disability program. His rehabilitation was not going well and he was not improving.

James had a negative history in his academic career as well. He was feeling rather hopeless about his future and his ability to support himself. He had been diagnosed with Learning Disabilities in school and had always felt he was a failure academically.

As a brawny high school football player, he had been pushed through courses in order to keep him on the team. In this new situation of nothing going for him, he desperately sought help from an NET/NEAT doctor.

Through NET, the doctor discovered an NEC dating back to the age of two years. At that time he had been inquisitive about a pot sitting on top of the stove. He pulled on it and the pot, filled with boiling water, spilled on his head. He learned that exploring was dangerous. The emotion of "fear" (of being inquisitive) was held in the kidney meridian access point.

James also discovered that learning was dangerous at the age of seven when his parents obtained a divorce. He had asked why they were divorcing. Their negative response to his question registered painfully that to ask or to express was dangerous. With this experience, another NEC of "paralyzed will" was located in the kidney.

All these NECs were cleared and his demeanor dramatically changed. The doctor observed earlier that James had been very opinionated about everything! In post-testing, he became Okay with having an opinion. His previous extremely opinionated stances had been a compensation for his "NOT OKAY" NEC of having an opinion!

The doctor happily reported that James is now attending college, maintaining a four point grade average, is much less opinionated, and is a happy young man with a healthy ego!

* * * * * * * * *

JESS

One doctor reported working with a nine-year old grandson of one of his NET/NEAT patients.

The grandson was in the third grade and had been diagnosed with Attention Deficit Disorder (ADD). The school system was evaluating him for this condition and referred him for all the prescription drugs normally utilized for this disorder.

The grandmother, through all her inner wisdom and love, believed Jess was not a problem child with a learning disability. Having experienced the technique herself, she insisted the doctor

treat him with the NET and NEAT process. When she brought him in for evaluation and possible treatment, the doctor reports:

> **"He could hardly look at me. He seemed to hold his hands, looking at them as though to find security there. He had a very non-emotional look on his face, a flat affect. I guess he was scared. I asked him if he wanted to play NET. His head moved just slightly up from the downtrodden position and his eyes moved ever so slightly, then he said 'ya'."**

The doctor asked Jess if he knew what low self-worth and self pride meant. Jess replied again with "ya." He then asked him , "So you know what it feels like when someone hurts your feelings by saying something or doing something to hurt you?" Again, Jess replied "ya," continuing to hold his head down in a distraught manner.

All the adults were watching him and the doctor had a strong feeling he was really struggling just to be there and go through with this procedure. Jess had not the slightest idea of what was about to take place.

The doctor began the NEAT, finding a Neuro Emotional Complex connected with love and his father. His father had been killed instantly in a truck accident when Jess was five years old. The NEC of "grief" was located in the right lung. Other NECs of "lost"

and "vulnerable" were found in the heart meridian. It was next discovered there had been an earlier time connected with his father. This time, Jess's system revealed the NEC of "paralyzed will" which was imprinted at age three when he was abused by his father.

The doctor discovered that the family had experienced a low financial period and had gone without food at that time. The father had beaten Jess and his mother in the midst of his own frustration. At this point in the process, Jess lifted his head as if he knew there was something good about his mind and body system that could reveal this experience.

The doctor was feeling deep compassion for this young boy and all that he had experienced thus far in his life. He asked Jess to feel how his father loved him and his arm went weak, indicating his system was incongruent with this statement.

It was then discovered that another NEC of "low self-esteem was localized in the spleen meridian. The NEC was about Jess feeling ashamed that his father did not show love to him. The NEC was cleared and the doctor reported, to his amazement, that this little fellow could take the beatings and the starvation, but had the NEC on not receiving love from his father.

Jess's grandmother brought him back in three weeks. She reported that he was no longer causing trouble in the classroom nor

fighting with the other students. The doctor asked him if he felt he was changing and he said "yes" and gave him the biggest smile!

They cleared out more issues of "low self-esteem" in the pancreas meridian, and "fear" in the right kidney meridian. The doctor told him he was making changes in his life and all he had to do was focus on the success he was having in school. Jess gave him another big smile and agreed. The doctor adds:

> **"It was great helping this young man see and feel the beauty of the world for perhaps the first time in his young life!"**

*** * * * * * * * * * ***

MIKE

Mike was another student whose early Emotional Reality deeply affected his later learning capacity. His mother brought him in to see Dr. Dustin Thomas, D.C., a certified NET doctor. He was an eight-year old boy who was being home schooled. His mother's present concern was that he was *not* doing well with his home schooling.

Through NEAT, Dr. Thomas discovered that Mike held an Emotional Reality imprinted at the age of five that *he was in jail!*

The underlying NEC was accessed and revealed there was a time in which Mike sat at the kitchen table to do his schoolwork. While doing his schoolwork, he looked through the rods or poles on the back of his chair. This scenario looked and felt to him that he was in jail. His reality was that everyone else could move about freely while he was confined behind the poles!

Dr. Thomas reported that the NEAT intervention with Mike resulted in great improvement in his academic endeavors. He no longer felt trapped in the learning process and, in fact, enjoyed his freedom and thus explored with natural curiosity. Learning then became an exciting endeavor.

Albert Einstein once said in his article "Never Stop Questioning":

> **"The important thing is not to stop questioning. Curiosity has its own reason for existing. One cannot help but be in awe when he contemplates the mysteries of eternity, of life, or the marvelous structures of reality. It is enough if one merely tries to comprehend a little of this mystery every day."**
>
> **"Never lose a holy curiosity."**

Many in our society have been the recipients of childhood overreactions and behaviors of well-intentioned adults who have stifled that innate curiosity and creativity.

And so, as we have seen in these few examples, it is well within the boundless power of this healing technique to reclaim that beautiful and wondrous holy curiosity.

* * * * * * * * * * *

CHAPTER SEVEN

NEURO EMOTIONAL ANTI-SABOTAGE TECHNIQUE AND ATHLETICS

"While it is true that
anxiety is the result of
having expectations...
it is even truer that
having anxiety is the result of
having an inability
to change expectations."

The Search for Self, One Man's Journey
~ Michael Grinder

All athletes know that to reach the top, one must work hard, practice hard, eat right, obtain professional advice, make sacrifices of all kinds, and believe in themselves. They do whatever they have to do to reach their goals at higher and higher levels. Sometimes, however, even when "all the right things" are utilized, some of the

best of them reach a level they cannot seem to go beyond, due to unknown blocks.

Dr. Mike Greenberg of Brentwood, California has been practicing for sixteen years, specializing in the natural care of athletic injuries. He regularly works with professional and world class athletes and has acted as a participating doctor at the 1984, 1988, 1992, and 1996 Olympics. At the last one, he helped runners Quincy Watts and Kevin Young achieve two world records and three gold medals. He also writes and speaks on sports chiropractic and has developed a line of innovative vitamins... all while maintaining a successful practice in Brentwood.

Regarding the above-mentioned blocks sometimes experienced by athletes, Dr. Greenberg states it well:

> **"Maybe you've hit that barrier. Your golf game has plateaued and more practice hasn't brought the desired results. You yearn to make that high velocity backhand, but every time you attempt your new back swing, your legs become Jell-O. It's as though you're driving into a roadblock and can't get past (it). But why? Who's the cop at the roadblock? Believe it or not, *YOU are.*"**

Dr. Greenberg describes what has happened to the body by saying that the body has grown accustomed to performing in a

particular way in response to certain triggers. The conditioned response is set up by repeated events, like Pavlov's dog. Normally, this is a good thing, as it allows the performance to become habit or an unconscious response. Dr. Greenberg gives this example:

> **"... an experienced outfielder doesn't have to think about putting up his glove to catch a fly ball. He's done that thousands of times since Little League. The action has become automatic, leaving him free to concentrate on the position and speed of the ball on that particular play."**

He continues:

> **"A runner doesn't think about putting one foot in front of the other. In fact, if she does think about every step, she may stumble over her own feet. She's better off letting that aspect of her performance 'go on automatic' while she focuses on strategy."**

Conditioning can create magnificence or it can create defeat. It works both ways and thus the conditioned response can hinder rather than help. There usually is a component that Dr. Greenberg calls a negative emotional trigger, or a Neuro Emotional Complex.

The NEC in sports, the emotional physiological reactions that sabotage success, *CAN* be changed!

Dr. Greenberg offers the following case histories from his files.

*** * * * * * * * * * ***

TONY

Tony was unusually small for a football player, several inches shorter, and quite a few pounds lighter than even the smallest ends. For years, he fought the odds and struggled to reach his dream... to play in the National Football League.

One day, when Tony came into Dr. Greenberg's office for a chiropractic checkup, Tony told him about the tryout he had the week before. He had caught every pass thrown his way and had run forty meters in 4.3 seconds. However, because of his size, he felt he was invisible to the scouts.

Tony related to Dr. Greenberg that he could feel his chance to play pro football slipping away, despite his marvelous performance. He had only one more chance (a tryout just three weeks away) to grab the attention of the NFL scouts and coaches.

Dr. Greenberg asked Tony if he thought that running forty meters in a tenth of a second less (4.2) would get him that draft

pick. When he jumped and shouted out "*yes!*", Dr. Greenberg told him flatly,

"TONY, I CAN HELP YOU RUN FASTER."

He told him about the Neuro Emotional Anti-sabotage Technique, explaining that it is a way to measure and change an unwanted conditioned response. He continued by telling him that when a physical trauma is combined with an emotional situation, the incident is stored in the body's memory. Later, when a similarly charged emotional situation occurs, the body will respond with a physical reaction much like the one brought on by the original trauma.

He explained that Chinese medicine, along with several schools of western psychology, had long recognized the link between emotions and the body. He spoke of the Oriental belief as a vital force or energy, called Chi in China and Ki in Japan, which flows through the body in channels (like those in which the blood and the lymph operate) called meridians. He continued by explaining that each meridian is linked to a certain organ, and that he would utilize the meridians to access information of any stored Neuro Emotional Complexes. After Dr. Greenberg told him about this technique, Tony exclaimed,

"WHY DIDN'T YOU TELL ME ABOUT THIS BEFORE NOW? LET'S GO!"

Dr. Greenberg began by testing Tony's belief system. That is, what he thought he could achieve. Even though he had given his best, he was open to possibility.

Dr. Greenberg asked Tony to repeat the following statement out loud, "I can run forty meters in 4.19 seconds." They found a weakness in the arm and when asked to say, "I'm without fear of losing," he also went weak. Dr. Greenberg treated the Neuro Emotional Complexes of "fear" in the kidney meridian and then "low self-esteem" in the spleen meridian.

A week after his last tryout, Tony flew into Dr. Greenberg's office looking radiant... and even taller! ***He had run the forty meters in 4.15 seconds!*** **That's arguably the fastest time in the history of the National Football League draft! And because he ran in tennis shoes instead of spikes, the time is not official. If Tony had run in spikes, Dr. Greenberg has no doubt he would have run even faster. Tony was drafted in an early round, made the team, and has been seen in the playoffs!**

This is likened to the words of Kahlil Gibran, who once wrote in ***I Care About Your Happiness*****:**

"A man can be free without being great,

but no man can be great without being free."

Freed from the Neuro Emotional Complexes, or conditioned responses from his past which blocked greatness, Tony is discovering and experiencing the utilization of his own inner resources. *For Tony, Neuro Emotional Anti-sabotage Technique has meant the fulfillment of a lifelong goal!*

* * * * * * * * * * *

YOUNG

In January of 1992, Dr. Greenberg started working with a group of excellent track and field athletes from the University of California at Los Angeles. This is the story of one of those young men.

This athlete was ranked fourth in the world in the four hundred meter hurdles for the past three years. He finished fourth in the Olympics in Seoul. When he came into Dr. Greenberg's office, he walked with his head down, having the look of defeat. The young man expressed his disappointment of not ranking first, feeling he was not reaching his potential, and wanted to be #1!

At first, Dr. Greenberg was not impressed by him, but Mrs. Greenberg told him he was the wisest of the group of athletes he was treating. In time, Dr. Greenberg learned not to sell him short.

After traditional chiropractic care, Dr. Greenberg figured, "Okay, it's time to focus on congruency and help him be a champion," but he found he did not need it! He was already congruent with being #1!

For a few nights, Dr. Greenberg tossed and turned trying to figure out what this athlete's problem was about. Finally, it came to him. If his problem was not about winning, it must be about *losing!*

The next time the young man came into his office, Dr. Greenberg positioned the arm of this world class hurdler straight out in front of himself, told him to hold it tight, then pushed down on that arm, simultaneously peppering him with a rapid fire sequence of statements. "You are a winner." "You can be the greatest hurdler in the world." "You are afraid of losing." Unlike the other strong responses, Young's arm collapsed with the last statement. Dr. Greenberg knew then that Young's problem was not in his aching back, but in his Body-Mind System.

Greenberg then discovered that Young had been traumatized by the disappointing fourth place at the Seoul Olympics in 1988. This resulted in "fear" localizing in the kidney meridian. After that, he was too anxious to run his best race. He was sabotaging himself

while he was dreaming of being number one. Subconsciously, he was believing he was no better than fourth!

Dr. Greenberg then cleared him for "It's okay to lose." One simple Neuro Emotional Complex. From that point on, he began to relax and improved in each race after that. This excellent athlete had not finished better than fourth place in any major international track meet in the previous four years.

> ***In the final race in Barcelona, he shattered Edwin Moses' world record in track and field at the Olympics!***

Young ran the four hundred meter intermediate hurdles in 46.78 seconds! That feat not only established Young as the greatest hurdler in the world, but it was a full second better than his previous PR! This quantum leap, to say the least, awed many throughout the track and field world!

Young himself credits it all to that day in Dr. Greenberg's office. Dr. Greenberg says:

> **"NET/NEAT promises to quickly identify and eliminate the hang-ups standing in the way of an individual's potential. NET works via a simple principle:**
>
> **'*THE BODY DOES NOT LIE*'!"**

When the subconscious is *NOT* congruent with the conscious, one will experience a temporary moment of weakness, i.e., *the body short circuits, the moment one unconsciously lies to the self.* The lying is not deliberate. In fact, while most of us have trained the brain to lie in certain circumstances, the body cannot/will not lie. The body will always reveal its truth. As Dr. Greenberg explains it, "The body does not always completely process the traumas that happen to it."

Over time, these unresolved emotions get triggered later in similar but inappropriate situations. When this conditioned response happens repeatedly, it blocks improvement and *you get stuck*, says Greenberg.

* * * * * * * * * * *

T.J.

This athlete, otherwise known as T.J., was twenty-two years old and had received approximately one hundred NET/NEAT treatments in a five month period. Dr. Greenberg reports the following in his experience with athletics and NEAT:

> **"The Neuro Emotional Anti-sabotage Technique is fantastic in track and field because you can**

quantitatively measure an athlete's improvement - for example, faster time."

Where did NEAT fit in for T.J.? Dr. Greenberg reports that almost every time he treated him over a five month period, especially prior to racing, he used the technique. Many of the Neuro Emotional Complexes centered around getting "Okay" with relaxing, being confident, and so forth.

The Olympic Games were the first international experience for T.J. Although he finished third at the United States Olympic Trials, T.J. was bouncy on the track. Dr. Greenberg hated to ask, but inquired if he was wearing the 6 mm heel lifts he had given him a few months back. T.J. replied he had lost the lifts when the Nike Company had given him new shoes. Dr. Greenberg treated T.J. with the Neuro Emotional Anti-sabotage Technique.

For the final race, T.J. broke the forty-three second barrier in the sixteen-hundred meter relay. The race was at 9:20 p.m. with a cross wind that was against the runners in the final stretch. T.J. ran a 43.1, *the fastest leg ever* in the history of track and field, helping the Americans to win a world record and Olympic Gold Medal. Dr. Greenberg reported:

> **"If the race had been held earlier with no wind factor, I am positive he would have broken the forty-three second barrier. Nike has now taken T.J. under their wing."**

As a result of NEAT, Dr. Greenberg and T.J. were able to influence the outcome of the Olympics. Tony, Young, and T.J. are only three of hundreds of athletes who have reached a higher level of performance thanks to Neuro Emotional Anti-sabotage Technique.

This technique can be used to increase achievement levels in all fields, not just athletics. Dr. Greenberg reports he has used the technique to cure "blocked" screen writers who are somehow unable to finish scripts, authors who cannot get started on their books, and actors who are hamstrung by rejections.

He reports treating one obese woman who could not lose weight because she was subconsciously afraid she would ruin her marriage by getting too much male attention. This related to an experience that happened to her when she was a slender adolescent, creating a Neuro Emotional Complex. One *can* find their real potential and, as Dr. Greenberg says, "*... and what you find might amaze you.*"

Dr. Greenberg also believes that through NEAT we can, as he states:

> ***"INFLUENCE THE WORLD BY RESTORING HARMONY AND HELPING PEOPLE TO BE HAPPY, ESPECIALLY TO OURSELVES!"***

In agreement with a multitude of others, Dr. Greenberg is quoted here as saying:

> ***"I feel Dr. Walker deserves a Nobel Prize for his work, and I want to thank God for this technique!"***

Dr. Mike Greenberg with two NEAT USA Olympic Gold Medalists

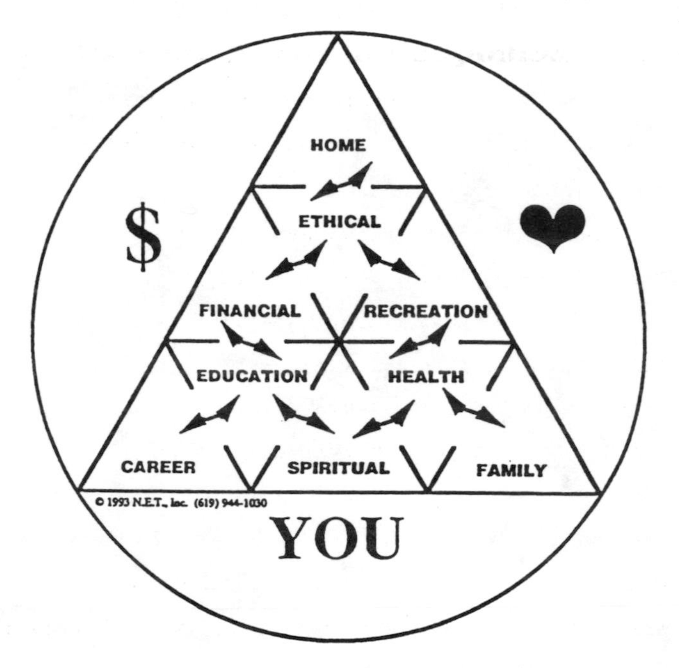

All is One - Life and Success require Balance

(Strengthen your weaknesses)

CHAPTER EIGHT

NEURO EMOTIONAL ANTI-SABOTAGE TECHNIQUE AND SPIRITUAL CRISIS

"If you bring forth what is within you,
what you bring forth will save you.
If you do not bring forth what is within you,
what you do not bring forth will destroy you."

The Book of Thomas
~Jesus Christ~

Throughout the history of man, we have pondered the condition or state of our existence. Countless numbers of philosophers, theologians, and psychologists have posed the questions, if not embraced the thoughts, concerning the woes, miseries, and challenges inherent in the state of being human.

In relationship to these questions, the subject of love is ever present. Some have postulated that we do not know the meaning of love and if we do not know the meaning of it, we do not then know

HOW to love. This thought is presented by Erich Fromm in his book, *The Art of Loving*, in which he states:

> ***"The awareness of human separation, without reunion by love... is the source of shame. It is at the same time the source of guilt and anxiety. The deepest need of man, then, is the need to overcome his separateness, to leave the prison of his aloneness. The absolute failure to achieve this aim means insanity."***

Others, like theologian Ruel Howe in *Man's Need and God's Action*, propose that the condition of man is that of loneliness, which is the result of *separation*. Modern psychology has partially described this condition in the term "separation anxiety."

Ruel Howe writes:

> ***"Sometimes our efforts to overcome our separation are made in alienating ways so that we accomplish the opposite of our intention."***

Specific faith or religious beliefs are NOT the point in regards to spiritual crises and Neuro Emotional Anti-sabotage Technique. What IS important is whether the Body-Mind System is congruent with whatever beliefs are or are not held. Ruel Howe's quote

speaks to the self-sabotaging that one is free to follow whatever path one chooses.

The following stories are case histories that exemplify those individuals who experienced "spiritual crises", and how Neuro Emotional Anti-sabotage Technique was utilized as the treatment of choice.

* * * * * * * * * * *

CAROL

Carol was in a spiritual crisis because one of her close friends had been told by an internationally known guru that when nodules and lumps appeared in her body, it was not cancer. Six months later, however, investigation by medical doctors revealed that her friend had metastatic cancer throughout her body. Carol was quite distressed about this situation concerning her friend and went to her doctor for treatment.

Utilizing the NEAT, her doctor found "anguish" in the right lung meridian as a result of feeling that both she and her friend had done "all the right spiritual things" and still her friend was "eaten up with cancer."

The original pattern dated back to age nineteen when Carol was in nursing school. At that time, electro-convulsive therapy (ECT) (sometimes more commonly known as "shock treatments") and

insulin shock therapy were being used. Carol believed in her "heart of hearts" that this was detrimental and absolutely unacceptable to her, but never voiced her opinion. As the Neuro Emotional Complex was discovered, she stated:

"I wanted to be a nurse so bad that *I sold my soul!*"

As she made this statement, she began sobbing uncontrollably. She sobbed for a full five minutes, over and over stating, "I sold my soul! I sold my soul! I sold my soul!"

The doctor discharged this NEC. In post-testing her, she discovered an original NEC in the bladder. This NEC revealed Carol, at the age of ten, being "miffed" at God because God had let her down.

Carol recounted her experience of confusion, disorientation, and "defusing" for the next two days following her neutralizing of the Neuro Emotional Complexes. She states she is now "relieved to the core!"

The doctor reported that on her next office visit, she was observed to be obviously relieved and very present and at peace about her friend and life in general.

*** * * * * * * * * * ***

MYRA

Myra also was in a spiritual crisis because of the same mutual friend (cancer diagnosis) mentioned in the previous case.

The same doctor treated Myra with NEAT, finding there was a Neuro Emotional Complex "dogmatically positioned" on the large intestine meridian. It originated at the age of twelve when Myra attended Catholic school.

Myra had taken a stand ("dogmatically positioned") that the Mother Superior at the school would not "get to her." Like her friend, Carol, the Neuro Emotional Complex was triggered by the friend's doing everything right and being so good.

The perceived belief of "it's not fair" led to Myra's original perception of the Mother Superior being unfair with the strict rules and the enforcement of them. This NEC had been triggered by the feeling of unfairness that God would let such a horrible thing happen to her friend who was dying of metastatic cancer.

Myra, although she still experiences grief, expressed relief and felt she could better cope with her friend's cancerous condition. The doctor reports Myra was visibly changed after her NEAT process as the lines on her face decreased, her posture straightened, and her voice was less strained.

* * * * * * * * * * *

MARIE

Marie had been longing to sing and act in the theater since she was a teenager. Now in her late fifties, her long held dreams were coming true. Marie had begun acting classes and had been cast in a very small part in a local community theater group's musical. She was quite happy about this!

The previous week, Marie had developed a dry, hacking cough. She also began to develop excess mucous in her sinus cavities and had achy feelings similar to the flu. On the second night of rehearsal, the hacking cough and other flu-like symptoms rendered her unable to adequately rehearse her musical piece appropriately.

The cough was worse the next day. That night, she reported staying awake "half the night" coughing incessantly. She used various remedies, including those that had always worked previously. Nothing would loosen the larynx or retard the cough.

The next day, she was treated in the doctor's office with NEAT. A Neuro Emotional Complex of "miffed" at God was discovered in the right kidney meridian point. This was imprinted at a very young age, relating to an experience with her father. The NEC was cleared, then she stared out into space and surprisingly stated,

"I am really pissed off!"

She was encouraged to get it out, to express her feelings, whereupon she began screaming at God, regurgitating all the pent-up, repressed emotions with,

> ***"I was doing everything right! I tried hard to make it come together! You didn't help me! You let me down! You let me down!"***

She went on until she had vented all her anger at God for not allowing her to have the career that she so deeply had wanted at a much earlier age.

> ***Within five minutes, Marie's cough was totally gone! And she went on with the rehearsals, unencumbered by the cough or the flu-like symptoms.***

* * * * * * * * * * *

JAN

Jan was participating in the same musical as Marie. During rehearsals, she began to feel tearful. Jan shared that for two and a half days, she had been weeping almost uncontrollably and was visibly having difficulty holding back the tears even as she spoke,

not knowing nor understanding what the tears were about. She sought assistance from her doctor, thinking she must be having a breakdown.

Dr. Nell Rodgers, a certified NET doctor, reassured Jan and began the NEAT process. Using this technique, she found a Neuro Emotional Complex of "anger" in the liver and gall bladder meridian. The NEC was originated at the age of nineteen when she was pregnant and did not want to be. She was angry with God for finding herself in this predicament. (Here again we find the individual crying, tearing, and thinking the NEC will be "grief" or "crying", but instead was actually imprinted as "anger", and the emotional response or behavior was that of crying.)

Immediately following the dis-charging of the NEC, Jan exclaimed:

> ***"That's amazing! The lump in my throat is gone! I don't feel like crying any longer! And I feel lighter!"***

Jan proceeded in rehearsals without the inconsolable crying, went on to give a fine performance, and has not experienced the "mysterious" emotional response since.

*** * * * * * * * * * ***

ANN

Ann was having some financial struggles. She was making it all right, but just barely keeping herself afloat. She worked very hard as a professional, single woman. She was well educated and even had a doctorate degree. She was well respected in her city and by most standards, was considered to be quite successful.

Ann, however, being a former minister's wife, was generous to a fault, both with her finances and her time for those who had need of her but could not afford her services. Ann had not planned well for herself financially. Now, as a single female, she had no savings to speak of and realized she could not work and give of the time she had done in the past.

Ann was nearing her late fifties and turned her thoughts to retirement and her dream of moving to the mountains, only to realize it would be years before that was possible, due to her large indebtedness. In retrospect, Ann recalled how many times in her life she had been on the brink of doing very well financially, and somehow things were reversed and she again found herself in debt. She turned to a NEAT doctor to assist her in this predicament. She was well aware of her self-sabotage in the financial arena.

Dr. Jane Lock of Royersford, Pennsylvania, worked with Ann, discovering an NEC of "abandoned" in the heart organ meridian.

The pattern of emotion was a belief that you cannot be prosperous and spiritual at the same time!

The NEC was traced back to the age of thirty-one. At that time, she felt joy and happiness as she fulfilled her dreams of having a family with three children. Three weeks after the birth of their third child, however, her minister husband told her he was having an affair. Later she discovered the affair was with one of their closest friends.

Another NEC on this was "anger and betrayal," which was held in the gall bladder organ meridian. The emotion was "betrayal" by husband, friend, and God for letting this horrible thing happen... especially since her husband was a minister!

Ann recalled how, so many years earlier, when she had held and nursed her three-week old son in her arms, her husband had told her about the affair. Though deeply wounded, shocked, and crushed to the core, she was determined to save the marriage... to keep the family together, no matter what the sacrifice or cost. She related that the next two years were interminably long as she struggled to do everything right as a mother of three small children, as a wife, and as the minister's wife. She feared that she had done something terribly wrong, that somehow it was all her fault that this nightmare had occurred!

Almost daily, her husband had switched from wanting a divorce, to the next day wanting to work the marriage out. She had become

terribly thin, developed colitis, and was living on medication to slow the colon overaction.

It became apparent, however, that the affair had continued throughout the following two years. Eventually, a child was born to the "friend" as a result of their affair. Ann reported feeling absolutely abandoned by God with this event, feeling deep despair, and yet somehow had a sense of being set free. She sought a divorce.

In Ann's family, divorce was a no-no, so this was particularly difficult for her to pursue. Dr. Lock discovered the NEC on this event was "can't figure it out," which was held in the adrenal meridian.

Another NEC of "deserted" was discovered in the heart meridian as she experienced the total negative judgment of the church members and the church, at large, for divorcing a minister! In their attempt to understand her actions, most of the parishioners and community members chose to believe that "*she* must be the one having the affair!"

Ann felt she was judged to be "the wicked witch from the west." One parishioner, whom she had thought to be a dear and close friend, refused to even look at her, much less speak to her.

To protect her children, thinking they need not know of this affair, Ann elected not to reveal the circumstances of the situation to the parishioners and the fellow clergymen.

When the Bishop called her personally to inquire as to the reason for the divorce, she was evasive. Ann had believed that in order to protect her children, she had to protect her husband, as well. Therefore, she simply replied to the Bishop's questions with, "We're simply incompatible, and there is no hope of reconciliation." A Neuro Emotional Complex of "dogmatically positioned" in the large intestine was revealed. Dr. Lock discharged the NEC on this event.

In the months that followed, Dr. Lock discovered and cleared many other NECs surrounding that period in her life. When she went for the original imprint, however, it was discovered that in-utero, around the gestational age of four months, there had been a male twin who was reabsorbed into the endometrium. When this was discovered, Ann collapsed, dissolving into tears!

Multiple NECs were uncovered surrounding these events. NECs of "abandonment" in the heart meridian point, "fear" in the kidney meridian point, "grief" in both lung meridian points, and "can't figure it out" in the thyroid meridian point... all were revealed and cleared.

The NECs had been recorded at a vulnerable time and, while living out her life, the imprinted NECs attracted like experiences. Then, during her marriage and divorce, the NECs became imprinted as "spiritual crises... separated," as Paul Tillich and Ruel Howell described, duplicating the in-utero experiences.

Ann reports that although she had done a great deal of traditional therapy and emotional work to heal the trauma of the marriage and resultant divorce, following the discovery of the "vanishing twin" (Vanishing Twin Syndrome), it has been a whole new ball game for her.

She reports that there have been far too many changes to mention them all. Through the years, Ann diligently sought to re-establish her spiritual connection and for the most part, did so. The most predominant change, however, has been her inner experience of joy and peace, her sense of mission and partnership with God, to serve, and to be "OKAY" with being prosperous, as well as spiritual.

And to add to that, she reports:

> **"My life feels so prosperous in the really important ways... of joy, peace, and love. In addition, I'm getting my debts paid off and have a secure financial plan I trust is working! Also, as we have cleared these NECs, my business has really picked up, and familial relationships are healing."**

* * * * * * * * * * *

CHAPTER NINE

NEURO EMOTIONAL ANTI-SABOTAGE TECHNIQUE AND RELATIONSHIPS

"Though it seems that you are traveling towards one another, the journey is within yourself. And though it seems you love another, it is self-love expressing. And what is beautiful is that you venture with the knowledge of the risk involved… the possible and painful hurt. And even if the risk is lost, you will journey again. Though the risk remains, now you know that you have the CAPACITY TO LOVE."

I Am

~ Michael Grinder

The conditioned response can create serious problems in relationships, as well as in other areas we have presented. Virginia Satir once said, to paraphrase, that there are not just two people who come to the marriage bed, but at the very least, six people. Those include the parents of both parties, to begin with. That

number can increase, depending upon circumstances such as deaths, divorces, former broken relationships, and so forth. What she was saying was that the conditioning influences of our lives determine our conscious, as well as unconscious, responses and reactions to the present circumstances.

From Andrew Salter, 1949, in *Conditioned Reflex Therapy*, we are given the following example of a conditioned response having a grave impact on one man's present situation. Salter says, to begin with:

> ***"The misguided and the well-meaning have tried to talk people out of their bodies for centuries. It can't be done."***

He continues by relating a case of an associate, Meignant, who presents the following:

> **"A thirty-five year old man, referred to as 'Mr. R,' had become sexually impotent six months earlier. He had sought professional health care assistance, but all treatments had failed to relieve the condition. He did remain potent with his wife, but only in hotel rooms and when they traveled. Six months earlier they had moved into a new apartment, and while something appeared familiar about the bedroom, he could not recall what**

it was.

Meignant, however, discovered that at a previous time, Mr. R had been caught in bed with a woman by a third person, who walked in and found them 'flagrante delicto.' They then discovered the pattern of wallpaper in the bedroom of the new apartment matched that of the bedroom in which he had previously been caught. When the wallpaper of the new apartment bedroom was replaced, his potency returned, and he happily functioned normally again!"

The following cases are examples of how the Neuro Emotional Anti-sabotage Technique affected various individuals' relationships, be they romantic, spousal, familial, or work-related situations.

* * * * * * * * * * *

SANDY

Sandy flew some distance for intense NEAT treatment, in a short period of time, with a certified NEAT doctor. Sandy was a psychotherapist who had worked long and hard on her own

emotional issues throughout the previous years. Both traditional and nontraditional therapeutic techniques were utilized in her search for solutions to her relationship problems.

Sandy presented herself as a very attractive, warm, and affectionate woman. As a thirty-nine year old divorced female, Sandy had always wanted to have a child. Motherhood had always eluded her. She presented with several relationship issues which she wanted to resolve.

Sandy's number one relationship problem was the opposite sex. She reported feeling that the man in her present relationship was not emotionally available to her. She also reported that she knew he was not emotionally stable or strong. Being quite aware of the discrepancy, however, Sandy could not bring herself to end the relationship. Since her divorce and prior to this relationship, she had very few romantic relationships in her life.

The second pressing problem concerned her financial status. She was a very successful therapist, working with the sexually abused and performing forensic work in the court system, as required in her caseload. Her financial situation was not what she desired, however, and no matter how hard she worked, somehow she just could not make her desired income.

Sandy was treated with NEAT. A Neuro Emotional Complex of "abandoned" was discovered at age two years and six months old. This was located in the heart meridian. At that age, her mother

had abandoned the family, and her father died soon thereafter with a broken heart.

The doctor had been aware of the long standing issues surrounding her parents, especially her mother. When she had spoken of her mother in the past, despite the years she had worked toward resolution, she always communicated distrust concerning her mother.

Following her father's death, she was placed in a convent and raised there. During her years in the convent, she was taught that money and spirituality don't mix.

The NEC was cleared, and she became OKAY with forgiving them and OKAY with being abandoned. (Remember, OKAY does not mean preference or that one likes something; merely that one's system is congruent with the situation and is no longer controlled by the "charge" surrounding the event.)

The next NEC discovered was "muddled instability" in the thyroid meridian, at the age of twenty-seven. Her spouse at the time had "muddled instability," and she was emotionally drained from being imprinted with this NEC of *his*.

Following this clearing of the emotion, she was OKAY being in emotionally healthy relationships, OKAY being emotionally and physically healthy herself, OKAY with having a child, and OKAY without having a child.

At the close of the NEAT treatment, Sandy reported feeling exhausted. At the same time, she felt very exhilarated, lighter, and mentally clear. Later, she reported terminating (with ease) the unhealthy relationship. Additionally, she also met and started dating three wonderfully healthy men and was having a blast!

These three men were all very attentive, sending her flowers and notes and generally being very emotionally present to her. Though she is a very attractive and intelligent woman, this was something she had never experienced! She exclaimed,

> **"Where are all these men coming from? I haven't changed my hair, clothes, or figure... and yet here they all are present in my life!"**

She spoke of her parents with much calm compassion and understanding. She reports feeling a real peace concerning them.

* * * * * * * * * * *

LOU

This attractive female executive came to one NEAT doctor, requesting help with releasing worry about her son and daughter-

in-law's marriage problems. She reported that they had a beautiful son who was "the apple" of her eye!

Lou's closeness to this "precious" grandson caused her to worry when she thought of the possibility of his parents divorcing and how he would be affected. There was so much worry that it affected her sleep pattern. Though she was a very resourceful and successful business woman, she felt she was having trouble coping with this situation.

A Neuro Emotional Complex of "muddled instability" was discovered imprinted in the thyroid meridian. When she was seven-years old, she had a teacher who held "muddled instability" about her job. Lou's system had picked this up and imprinted with the same NEC.

Another NEC was discovered when she was thirty-three years old. This was "fear" localized in the right kidney meridian access point and had to do with her fear that her spouse would be unable to care for their children in an emotionally supportive way.

Following these clearings, Lou reported feeling "tingles of energy." She felt her blood circulating in her veins, lighter, and much happier.

Lou became OKAY with her grandson, whether or not his parents divorced.

Later, Lou reported that she had been sleeping like a log! She was coping with everything much better, not just her son's marriage problems, but also the business and other community groups and projects with which she works.

Additionally and happily, Lou further reported that her son and daughter-in-law have resolved their issues. She now enjoys both her oldest grandson and his new "precious" little brother, who was born during the parents' difficult period!

* * * * * * * * * * *

JOHN

John, an eighteen-year old college freshman, attractive and intelligent, came into the doctor's office with his mother, who had already experienced NEAT. He was most curious about the technique.

John reported that he was in a relationship with a girl whom he was having difficulty trusting. It seemed to be a repeat pattern in his relationships with girls.

Investigating his system, the doctor uncovered a Neuro Emotional Complex of "abandonment," localized in the heart meridian. Although his parents had been divorced when he was much younger, the NEC was not about the divorce, as might be expected. It concerned his older brother. In John's emotional reality, his older brother "abandoned" him when he went to live with his biological father. John was thirteen years old at that time.

These NECs were discharged as John broke a sweat and exclaimed:

> **"I hadn't thought of that in years, and now I remember that's exactly how I felt then!"**

In the post-check, John became OKAY with trusting himself in relationships and OKAY with or without "abandonment." He expressed how good he felt. He was amazed that he had not needed to verbalize anything and still this event was discovered.

At the time of the event, he knew that his brother moving away had deeply affected him, but stated he was amazed that it was triggered by his inability to trust his present girlfriend.

John reported later that he is doing very well in school and great with life in general. His mother, some time later, reported that John broke up with the former girlfriend following his NEAT session.

Not long afterward, he began dating a girl whom his mother called an angel and felt to be more compatible with John. She stated:

> **"John trusts this girl... they really have fun, are so happy, and the family really loves her, too!"**

At the time of this writing, his mother announced John and his "angel" were recently married. She added that all of them are thrilled about the happy union.

* * * * * * * * * * *

JANET

While attending a music seminar, Janet developed pain in her tailbone. She was having difficulty sitting in the chair, so she moved to a pillow on the floor. She had difficulty sitting there, as well. As the day progressed, walking became difficult. She sought treatment from Dr. Nell Rodgers, a certified NEAT doctor.

Using NEAT, Dr. Rodgers discovered an NEC. Her muscle tested weak with the declaration, "I am ready, willing, and able to give up my pain." The NEC was related to the emotion of "miffed" at the current time, localized in the kidney meridian. Janet's daughter was "miffed" because Janet would not resolve the tension and conflict with her ex-husband. Janet was sensitive to her daughter's feeling of "miffed" and thus was imprinted with that NEC from her daughter.

The next NEC was discovered with therapy localization of the painful area. (The doctor touches the painful area in combination with the emotional points on the forehead.) This pattern went back

to age twenty and the emotion of "anguish" in the lung organ meridian regarding the feeling that God had let her down.

It was Janet's reality that she had been doing everything right, trying to serve God, yet her life was in chaos. She had to move away at that time, and her schooling ended.

It was also then that Janet discovered for the first time ever who her biological father was... and that he was now dead! Additionally, her mother and stepfather coerced her into moving to Atlanta, where she did not want to be. The second emotion of this event was that she was "miffed" at God for letting her down.

The next NEC was discovered in the statement "ready, willing, and able to accept the *goodness* of giving up my pain". As soon as this statement was made, the doctor reported that the pain spontaneously worsened. The NEC was on the right kidney meridian and the emotion was "wishy-washy" concerning a current situation. This was the result of her inner conflict about totally cutting off her ex-husband and refusing to resolve conflicts.

The next NEC was discovered on the declarative "ready, willing, and able to give up my *stubbornness* of letting go of my pain". This pattern dated back to age ten when Janet was "miffed" (again, localized in the right kidney meridian) that she had to move away from her grandmother. She loved her grandmother dearly and felt she was one of the few people who loved her. The doctor cleared all of these NECs.

Following this final release, the pain was completely gone from Janet's derriere! She smiled one of the biggest smiles ever and exclaimed, "*That's incredible!*" She began dancing to the music that was playing during the seminar lunch.

In Janet's case, we observed (as is very common) many NECs which are connected or stacked, as though in preferential lineage. The body/mind wisdom appears to present information of fixated emotions in quite an orderly fashion, sometimes in what one would not consciously reason to be the case. We discover with NEAT that things are often not as they appear. Pertaining to this seeming phenomenon, Dr. Walker states:

> **"There is a conscious and unconscious mind powered by the Innate. We *are* Innate Intelligence."**

* * * * * * * * * * *

HARRIET

Harriet, a seventy year old patient, entered the office as a new patient. She was a minister's wife, a gentle, Southern, Christian woman. She limped and leaned to one side, almost unable to bear any weight on her right leg. Harriet was diagnosed with four disc

protrusions. She decided to see a NEAT doctor before undergoing more severe therapy or surgery.

Four days into her new treatment, it was discovered she had Neuro Emotional Complexes related to her limp and pain. The emotions were now priority. Her physician was concerned about how she would receive the technique.

Her doctor explained as best she could the connections between emotional components and one's Emotional Realities, which were influencing the system and in her case, the physical body. Somewhat resistant, Harriet agreed to continue.

It was discovered that there had been some resentment about her father at age ten. Harriet resisted the notion initially, as she insisted that her father was always wonderful to her.

Finally, Harriet stated with much encouragement, "The only thing I can remember is that I wanted him to buy me some shoes, and he said, 'No, it's Sunday. The stores are closed'." As she repeated that statement, her arm went weak. A Neuro Emotional Complex of "bad memory" was discovered in the right kidney meridian. The NEC was cleared.

Harriet then responded, "Well, it could have been when I was seven years old, instead of ten. That is when my baby sister was killed."

The doctor further investigated this story and discovered that Harriet's family had always visited a certain place after church on

Sundays. On a particular Sunday, the usual "nanny" was not present to care for the children. It was then that the family tragedy, which had deeply and unconsciously affected Harriet, unfolded. On that Sunday, Harriet's two and a half year old sister had slipped away and toddled over to the family car. The door was locked, so her little sister went around to the driver's side door in the street. It was there that she was struck by an oncoming automobile. Baby sister was taken to a hospital, but died later that night.

Harriet was asked to picture the worst part of that incident. She recalled her mother frantically asking others if they had seen a little girl in a pink dress. Someone told her that a child wearing a pink dress had been hit by an automobile. As she recalled her mother screaming and moaning, "My baby, my baby, my baby!" Harriet's system went totally weak.

In addition to this traumatic picture, Harriet recalled that she was not permitted into the hospital to see her sister who, she was told, was asking to see her. The NEC was "anguish" stored in the lung meridian. As the emotion was cleared, Harriet sighed deeply, stating, "I had not thought of that for years."

Harriet expressed that she felt as though a huge weight had been lifted off her back. She walked upright with a steady, even gait out of the office. She no longer leaned and no longer was in pain!

* * * * * * *

PAM

Dr. Glenn Strobel from Norberth, Pennsylvania, reported Pam, a mother of a young girl, was treated in his office for neck pain due to an auto accident. The condition was resolving, except for moderately severe neck pain in the right lateral plexus. On a scale of zero to ten, ten being the most severe pain, her pain was at a seven.

Dr. Strobel discovered and diagnosed a Neuro Emotional Complex of "over concern" for her daughter. The NEC was found doing myofacial technique, a Neuro Emotional Extra Technique (NEXT was developed by Dr. Walker).

Pam's "over concern" was connected to the stomach meridian access point. Pam said that her daughter was a "pain in the neck" and that she was worried about her. Dr. Strobel cleared the NEC of "over concern."

After Dr. Strobel cleared the NEC, Pam's pain dropped from a seven down to between a zero and one. She continues to improve and believes she will get to a constant of zero pain.

* * * * * * * * * * *

AMY

This female patient experienced anxiety attacks every weekday afternoon at four o'clock. She knew that the source of these attacks was her early childhood experiences. Her mother always returned home from work at that time, and Amy was required to have the house cleaned and orderly or she would be in serious trouble!

This anxiety had been experienced for twenty years at four o'clock... only on weekdays! Amy sought multiple therapies through the years. All had been unsuccessful in obtaining relief. She sought assistance and treatment from Dr. Tate Rolfs in Kaneohe, Hawaii.

Utilizing NET, Dr. Rolfs began the search by asking Amy to hold the "snapshot" in her mind of an anxiety attack at precisely four o'clock. With this in focus, he traced the emotion back to the age of seven. The emotions of "fear" and "paralyzed will" were imprinted in the left kidney organ meridian access points. Dr. Rolfs moved into NEAT, asking her to repeat the following statements as he muscle tested her:

> **"I'm OKAY with my mother's displeasure with me."**
> **"I'm OKAY being in trouble with my mother."**
> **"I'm OK with my mother returning home at four o'clock."**
> **"I'm OKAY with being responsible for the house."**

Her muscle went weak on all of these statements. In this searching, it was discovered there was a time when she had not met her mother's expectations of having the house in order when she returned from work. Amy's emotional reality of that event revealed the experience of being in big trouble! Amy's body began to tremble as this memory was brought to the surface.

Another NEC of "abandoned" was next located in the heart meridian access point, followed by "dogmatically positioned" in the large intestine meridian access point. Amy was sensitive to her mother's "dogmatically positioned" emotion with which Amy had been imprinted!.

The next emotion discovered was a Neuro Emotional Complex of "grief" located in the right lung meridian. Amy's body became very flushed and warm. Dr. Rolfs discharged all these NECs in a fifteen minute session.

Amy's immediate response was relief, after shedding a few tears. Amy checked OKAY and maintained a strong muscle on all the above-listed statements. She has experienced NO anxiety attacks since her session three years ago!

Amy now calmly moves through the four o'clock hour without even a smidgeon of anxiety or nervousness. She expressed her extreme gratitude and thought how much better her life would have been had NET and NEAT been available to her years earlier!

* * * * * * * * * * *

MAGGIE

Maggie was a sixty year old female who lived in Hawaii with her husband. Her presenting problem was that she could not fly in an airplane without extreme agitation, nervousness, and anxiety.

Maggie and her husband had accepted this behavior pattern for their entire marriage of more than forty years. It had interfered significantly with their lives. They wanted to travel more to see their children on the mainland in their retirement years.

In desperation, Maggie made an appointment with Dr. Rolfs one day before a scheduled one month trip to the mainland. Both Maggie and her husband were worried about the anxieties that would occur on the long flights.

With NEAT, Dr. Rolfs discovered the emotion of "fear" located in the left kidney meridian which was imprinted at the age of three. Maggie was a passenger in the car her mother was driving. The day was beautiful when they started out. Bad weather suddenly appeared, and the driving visibility was greatly reduced. Maggie's mother was quite frightened. The situation worsened when a small animal, unseen, ran across the road, and the car struck the animal. Maggie, sensitive to her mother's emotion, was imprinted by her "fear" and "paralyzed will".

Next, Dr. Rolfs discovered the NEC of "sadness" located in the lung meridian relating to the same incident. He quickly dis-charged these NECs with NEAT.

Upon returning from the plane trip, Maggie excitedly reported absolutely no problems with anxiety, nervousness, or agitation when flying! It was not until well into the trip that they even noticed the absence of the anxiety.

Maggie related that she had also been healed of her other chronic problem (not previously mentioned to Dr. Rolfs). She reported that she had never been able to drive through fog in a car. This was quite a problem in Hawaii. In order to drive into town, one frequently had to drive through the cloudy mists on the beautiful mountains.

This imposed a great hardship for her on Oahu. Maggie reported that prior to the NEAT intervention with Dr. Rolfs, she would have to sit in her car and wait for a weather change to clear the mist/fog. Often she was stuck for hours.

After a single treatment, Maggie could not stop exclaiming, with weepy eyes, "I can go through the fog now! I can go through the fog now!" All of this was accomplished in a twenty minute session!

As can be seen in many of these cases, the individuals were imprinted by their parents' emotions. As children, we are highly sensitive. Without so much as a verbal expression, we can pick up or tune in to someone else's emotion and be imprinted with it. Most commonly, when imprinted as children, these NECs are from parents or significant adult role models.

* * * * * * * * * * *

SARA

Sara sought treatment with Dr. Jim Hogg in Davenport, Iowa, for relief of lower back pain. Although Sara followed other therapies religiously, and gained some relief, she still suffered long-standing chronic pain.

Dr. Hogg traced the lower back pain to love of a female friend at the age of seventeen. The emotion was "dogmatic position" located in the right lung meridian access point.

In searching with NEAT, Dr. Hogg discovered Sara's NEC was in the category of "self." It was Sara's issues and multiple conflicts about females in student politics (i.e., bra burner vs. being a more traditional feminine pink lady). In her "dogmatic position" NEC, she was the fluffy housewife who had given up the fire, so to speak.

Sara had issues surrounding being self-completed, asking for and accepting help from others. Dr. Hogg traced back to a broken arm in 1993 and discovered "grief" in the lung organ meridian.

The original time of this emotional imprint was in-utero. At that time, there was "grief" in exposing herself to God, relating to God, feeling lack of choice or free will, and so forth. Dr. Hogg discharged the NECs and prescribed an NET homeopathic remedy.

Sara experienced immediate relief from the chronic lower back pain. As seen often, if the NEC is found to be the precipitating factor in vertebral pain, when the NEC is discharged or cleared, the misaligned vertebrae will adjust on their own. Also, when there are pains emanating from other parts of the body, and NECs are identified as the source of the pain and cleared, the pain is then relieved and often totally alleviated.

* * * * * * * * * * *

POLLY

Polly had a problem dealing with the stress of driving in heavy traffic. She would get so upset and angry with rude and discourteous drivers that she would experience a headache and generally would feel bad all over.

After being a manager for a clerical and data entry group for fifteen years, Polly's position disappeared due to automation of her company. The vice president of the company placed Polly in a position for which she was not suited and in which she felt unable to handle.

After five months of doing her best to learn hardware and software terms, struggling to acquaint herself with the new job, he told her she was not trying hard enough. He placed her in another group. Her salary was cut drastically, and she lost all management benefits.

Although she loved her new job in the new group and found that she was well suited for it, she could not let go of the resentment and hurt. She had forgiven the mistreatment, but could not forget it.

Polly reported that it "ate" at her all the time, and she felt consumed by feelings of anger and resentment. These feelings built up until it affected her entire outlook on life. It was difficult for her to see the vice president every day and be polite to him. Polly sought treatment from Dr. David Hoover, a certified NET doctor in Ft. Worth, Texas.

Dr. Hoover asked Polly to visualize the vice-president and the situation created by his actions. She immediately presented with a weak muscle. He discovered "anger" and "resentment" emotions localized in the liver and gall bladder meridian access points. These dated back to a childhood experience where she really did her best in a task, was ignored, and in fact, was chastised. Polly felt punished for something she had felt good about. She felt that she was not valued for her efforts. Dr. Hoover cleared these emotions and then discovered "disgust" in the stomach meridian access point. This NEC was related to the same event. Polly felt "disgust" with

the response of those "in charge" at that time. This emotion was also cleared by Dr. Hoover, using NEAT.

After this treatment, Polly experienced acceptance of her new assignment and release of the anger and resentment. Polly reported:

> **"I will never forget the peace and calm that I felt after that session. It was like the anger and resentment just melted away. The calmness and peace I felt have stayed with me, and I no longer feel dread when I have to interact with this person."**

And she further added:

> **"I have used (been treated by) NEAT three times with great success. I don't understand how it works... I just know that it does! It would be very beneficial to anyone going through a stressful time in their life or for just ordinary everyday problems. I would recommend NET for anyone dealing with emotional situations in their life, whether they be large or small!"**

* * * * * * * * * * *

Robert

Robert was an eleven-year old boy at the time he was brought by his parents for treatment (also with Dr. Hoover). He had never been able to sleep alone at night in his own bedroom.

When Robert was a baby he was very sickly and his crib was in his parent's bedroom. As he grew older he had an incessant need to sleep in his parent's bedroom. He would be put to bed in his own room, only to drag his sleeping bag through the house to mom and dad's room and sleep on the floor. With all his parents' efforts in working with this problem, the best they were able to accomplish was his sleeping under a table in his parent's bedroom on top of a sleeping bag.

Robert was embarrassed by this behavior and wanted to give his mother a "Christmas present" of being able to sleep in his own room at night. This would give both his parents and himself more privacy.

Dr. Hoover requested Robert to get into the feeling mode and to see a picture of his sleeping in his own bed in his own room. In doing this, Dr. Hoover discovered the emotion of "fear" stored in the right kidney meridian.

The ensuing history revealed that both his parents cleaned offices at night and an older sister had taken care of Robert when he was much younger. She had told him that if he was not good his

parents would not come home! His fear as a pre-schooler was that his mom might leave and not tell him where she was going!

Dr. Hoover discharged this NEC and post-tested to check for clearance with statements to "surround the dragon."

After the clearing, Robert tested with a strong muscle for the previous weakness on his "feeling mode" or emotion of "fear" about sleeping alone in his own bed in his own room. He also checked strong with feeling safe to, deserving to, and believing he could be honored by sleeping in his own bed.

The very night of this NEAT process, Robert was able to sleep in his own bed. Since the time of this writing he has slept there every night. He's a proud eleven year old and his parents were very appreciative of his Christmas present.

* * * * * * * * * *

I am particularly and consistently impressed with the rapid healing properties and impact NEAT has upon children! The psychological problems that could have developed during Robert's adolescent years are immense, had this problem not been corrected.

It is with deep gratitude and amazement that I observe children responding so quickly to this technique.

The deep sensitivity and attachment of the child to the parent is again exemplified in the following case story of Bryan.

* * * * * * * * * *

BRYAN

Bryan was a young man, aged twenty-eight. He was a sales representative for a large international company. By conventional standards he did okay making approximately $4000 per month. He was frustrated because he had been to many seminars on how to better himself in his profession and how to sell his particular products.

Bryan attended a lecture that Dr. Howard Cohn, a Certified NET doctor, of Costa Mesa, California, presented on NET and NEAT. Several people were present at the lecture who had been treated by Dr. Cohn. Bryan spoke with them about the technique. Their responses were all very positive about the results. Bryan decided to try NEAT for the long sought-after financial breakthrough.

When Dr. Cohn checked Bryan, he weakened on "It's safe to make more than $4000 a month." The emotion was "expanded importance of self" and was located in the stomach.

Dr. Cohn traced it back to age fifteen when Bryan found out that his dad made $4000 a month. He had never made more than that amount, and was proud of that achievement. Bryan's system interpreted that if he made more than $4000 in a month that it would invalidate and dishonor his dad and his dad's success.

Additionally, this would make him more important than his dad which would be disrespectful. Dr. Cohn cleared the NEC.

The next month Bryan sent Dr. Cohn a copy of his monthly bonus check for the amount of $8200. He had worked in his company for two and one half years, never making more than $4000 a month prior to his NET session!

* * * * * * * * * *

In the following chapter we will look at the healing impact of NEAT/NET on victims of violence, trauma, and evil.

CHAPTER TEN

NEAT/NET HEALING VICTIMS OF VIOLENCE AND TRAUMA

"The journey into darkness has been long and cruel, and you have gone deep into it."
Course in Miracles

The world has been riveted to the news media reporting atrocities so shocking that we find them unfathomable. Human beings by the thousands have been lined up and massacred in Africa reminding us of Hitler's diabolic rampage in Europe.

We are pierced with pain in our viewing of the thousands of tearful and shocked refugees who have been forced to flee and leave their homes, families, and belongings in Kosovo and Yugoslavia. Their homes being burned, all personal identification destroyed, they struggle on in tent cities with inadequate health care, food water, and sanitation facilities. Families are separated and fear the worst for the possibility of re-uniting. They cling desperately to hope.

Closer to home we view in horror our children killing one another in schools across our nation. The purported intentions of

destruction by the Columbine High School students are horrific beyond imagination!

The world continues to ask the all too important questions. How could such things happen? How could we have overlooked the clues to these impending disasters? How could our youth be so filled with fear, hatred, and non-feeling as to act out such deeds? And finally what can we do to prevent such events from manifesting in the future?

Yes, there are portraits of evil that impact our world, society, communities, and families. Richard K and Paula Saxon Nongard, in their book *Evil Stands Alone*, use the term "Praxeological Evil" to define the core essence of some people.

One of the most brilliant and original thinkers of the Age of Reason, the eighteenth century theologian Emanuel Swedenborg, states in his book *Heaven and Hell!*

> ***"The reason we are united in spirit to both***
> ***Heaven and Hell is to keep us in freedom."***

The paradox in the quality of human existence is apparent. Free Will is one of our greatest gifts as Creations of the Creator. Without it we would be mere robots...the same, alike, no differentiation, no special gifts or creativity.

Perhaps the following will offer enlightenment in the midst of such darkness.

BEAUTY, LOVE, JOY, AND FEAR

Torkom Saraydarian, in his book *The Flame of Beauty, Culture, Love, Joy* lists twelve main obstacles of love and joy:

1. **Pressure… forcing your will upon the will of others; weakens love and joy.**
2. **Jealousy...it wants to possess; it dissipates love and joy, and loses his life.**
3. **Denial of Freedom...of other persons; this distinguishes the flame of love and joy.**
4. **Misuse People and their belongings...exploitation rests in the heart; love and joy evaporate.**
5. **Non-inclusiveness…is self-worship, separation; breeds aggressiveness, hate, and conflict.**
6. **Unrighteousness...in thoughts, emotional responses, and actions; will not have real joy in your heart, and love will never bloom.**
7. **Ugliness...makes beauty disappear; love and joy fades away in ugly thoughts.**
8. **Insincerity...love and joy can not exist where sincerity is absent.**

9. Criticism...creates rejection, aura hardens in its periphery, imposes your personality on others; your Soul hardly finds a chance to shine out.

10. Nosiness...criticizes, judges, imposition of thoughts; cannot gain your freedom.

11. Carelessness and pride...go together; leads one to irresponsibility; is separative, belittles others, repels all joy and love.

12. Attachment...to any love-object makes you lose your joy and your love for that object will bring great disappointment. Only through non-attachment to your love-object, can you perpetuate your love and joy."

Joy is a characteristic of love. Joy is a special wisdom. The presence of love makes us aware of why we are here. We share lovelessness, in our individual and collective hells, created by fear.

Fear is expressed as abuse, corruption, violence, war, greed, rape, addiction, control, evil, and manipulation. The *Light of Love* shines within us! It can only be hidden...not destroyed! When the sun is darkened it is because we have not chosen Love. When the moon is darkened, it is because we have not chosen Faith. When the stars are darkened, it is because we have not chosen Joy.

In this chapter, the end results of *fear* will be presented. The violent actions, by those who have allowed their *Light of Love* to become so hidden, demonstrate the acting out of their deepest fears upon their victims, creating the deepest of pains.

The first case cited here is one who was a casualty of war. Greed spawned by fear, then leads to war.

These cases are about those who have healed their deepest nightmares. In their journeys back from severe trauma, violence, and the dark night of the soul, they are the fortunate ones who have experienced NEAT and NET.

* * * * * * * * * * *

JOE

Joe was a veteran of the Vietnam War and lived in Hawaii. For twenty four years, he suffered from combat dreams... or nightmares. In these dreams, he would scream out, "They're coming to get me! They're coming to kill me! They're coming to maim me!!"

Joe reported that the countryside was ugly and sinister in the dream setting. His roommates reported that he often screamed in his sleep, and they were unable to calm or control him. No other therapies, pharmaceuticals, nor treatment had released this man

from his own personal agony. Dr. Tate Rolf and Gary Smith worked with this tormented veteran utilizing NEAT.

Many NECs were discovered that were imprinted during his time of military service in the Vietnam War. There were numerous atrocities experienced... far too many to uncover on the first visit! Dr. Rolf and Gary Smith moved quickly to spare Joe the deeply emotional revisits to those experiences.

"Fear" that felt more like terror was located in the kidney meridian access points; "anger" in the liver and gallbladder meridian points; "sadness" and "grief" in the lung meridian points... all were discovered to be related to his Vietnam experiences. These emotions were quickly and compassionately cleared.

Happy and relieved, Joe reported that after the NEAT treatment, his nightmares were transformed. The dreams continued to be of Vietnam, but instead of the horror of impending doom, they came to help and to save him!

Additionally, the countryside in the dreams became beautiful and peaceful, as opposed to the prior setting of ugly and sinister. Joe's roommates reported that he no longer screams and shouts in his sleep.

Overall, we have not really known how to successfully assist our war veterans in adjusting and recovering from the atrocities they endured in that tragic war.

NET/NEAT has become an avenue by which hundreds of such veterans have recovered from Post Traumatic Stress Syndrome. "Recovered" is described here as a transformation. Memories of the horrors experienced still remain. However, through treatment with this technique, the NECs are discharged and the negative charge of the remembered events evaporate. These veterans have been given a second chance to re-enter life as functional, healthier, and happier human beings.

* * * * * * * * * * *

Family violence in the United States is occurring at an increasingly alarming rate! Alcohol and drug abuse, sought after to anesthetize the internal/inner unresolved pains, are some of, if not the major contributing factors, to this violence.

The drugs and/or alcohol anesthetizes the inner unresolved pain. Whatever self controls that were in place are soon dissolved. Significant others become targets of the perpetrator's regurgitation of their pains through violence.

The following case illustrates this sickness within our society.

* * * * * * * * * * *

JENNIE

Dr. Walter Jaakkola of Parker, Colorado had treated Jennie for three years for heavy metal toxicity. He utilized nutrition as the primary treatment mode. Jennie was a forty eight year old, married female with four children.

Jennie appeared one day for her regular appointment, nearly crawling into his office. She was experiencing severe muscle spasms and spinal pain. Crying, she reported feeling like she had been hit by a car!

Jennie had night sweats and severe abdominal cramps. She had not slept for one full week and had been so miserable that she hoped she would die. Thoughts came to her about how she might kill herself.

Dr. Jaakkola had just returned from his first NET Basic Training. He decided to do just what Dr. Walker recommended... "jump right in" with the NET first thing Monday morning. Jennie was his first patient of the day.

Dr. Jaakkola found that there was an emotion related to the spasm and pain. The first Neuro Emotional Complex was "grief" located in the right lung meridian. This was in the "love" category and pertained to her father.

(NOTE: Remember, there are three basic categories in

which we search for the NECs.

1) The Money Category, i.e., money, job, finance, career, places, things, time, space, energy, the material things in life.

2) The Love Category, i.e. everyone you have ever loved, everyone that has ever loved you.

3) "You"and "what about you" in any framework, such as "you the woman," "you the son,", "you friend,"... or "you" in any situation.)

As Dr. Jaakkola worked with Jennie, the story unraveled. She had been raped by her drunken father when she was fourteen years old. Furthering this event, in his drunken state, he picked up a machine gun and threatened to kill the entire family.

Dr. Jaakkola quickly discharged the NECs and was amazed by the results! Immediately following his NET treatment, without any other adjusting, Jennie's pain was eighty percent relieved. With three more visits, she had no more pain nor problems associated with the spasms.

Dr. Jaakkola added another interesting anecdote. He had treated her heavy metal toxicity for three years with only mild improvement. Following the NET treatment, he placed her on the homeopathic NET remedy "Metal" for the lung meridians. She

began to rapidly clear the metal toxicities which had plagued her for the past three years.

* * * * * * * * * * *

ANGIE

Angie was a young, single, female professional. She experienced substantial shock when she lost her job in 1994. She decided to take a week off and visit her sister in San Diego before looking for another job.

While in California, she was caught in the Los Angeles earthquake... another shock! She was not injured severely. She was grateful to return home safely, even though traumatized by the experience. The new year of 1994 had certainly come in with a "big bang" for her!

Angie was back home, alone, on a Saturday night at the end of January. She was diligently filling out job applications. Around eleven o'clock, she decided to turn out the light and go to sleep. It was dark and stormy outside. Rain was accompanied by thunder and lightning.

Angie closed her bedroom door so that her cat would not awaken her by jumping on her bed during the night. All the other doors and windows in the house were securely locked.

Angie awakened about four thirty in the morning. It was still storming outside. She was lying in bed, thinking about a weird dream she just had when her bedroom door opened. At first, she thought it was her cat. When she didn't jump on to the bed, Angie sat straight up.

Although the room was dark, she determined that there was a person crawling into her bedroom. She called, "Mike, is that you?" thinking that her boyfriend had returned early from a trip into San Francisco and was playing a joke on her. She attempted to turn on the bedside lamp, but discovered there was no electricity.

Suddenly, the person on the floor jumped on the bed and hit her twice on the head with a club! Terrified and shocked, she screamed out the mantra (a form of prayer) for danger. As she struggled to push the attacker off, he shouted, "Shut up, bitch! Shut up, bitch! Shut up, or you'll get this knife!" Angie felt the cold hunting knife poke into her chin! And Angie became obediently silent.

The attacker pushed her up into a sitting position. "What are you going to do to me?" she asked. "Tie you up," was his reply. "Yes, tie me up, rape me, kill me...," were Angie's terrified thoughts. She began to reclaim composure and thought of survival. Somehow or other, she had to get the window open.

Angie sensed that he had put the knife down. She grabbed the phone. He knocked it out of her hand, and they wrestled. He

grabbed her arms and turned her toward the window. "Perfect position!" she thought.

Angie seized the opportunity and kicked with both feet as hard as she could. The window glass shattered as she screamed "911! 911! Angie, 911!"

Scurrying quickly through the window, she escaped from her attacker! The rain on her face and the fresh night air felt heavenly as she ran to the neighbor's house. Angie ended up with forty stitches... but she was ALIVE!

The following weeks were extremely difficult. She lost fearlessness, which she had always possessed. Every little sound now made her jump. During the scuffle that night, her neck was wrenched.

A friend told her to go see Dr. Linda Powers. Angie wondered if the doctor would take care of her and could only trust that the Victims of Violent Crimes Program would reimburse Dr. Powers. Without a job, Angie had no insurance and no money to pay for treatment.

Dr. Powers turned out to be extremely compassionate, treating Angie three times per week. In addition to relief from the pain in the wrenched neck, Angie wanted to be free from the fear of being at home alone. The friend who referred her to Dr. Powers spoke of this new technique that might really help her with the emotional trauma.

Dr. Powers examined her and began NEAT treatment. She discovered the expected emotions of "fear" and "bad memory" in the kidney meridians and cleared them immediately.

Following NET and NEAT treatments, Angie's neck healed, and she regained her fearlessness. She now has a new job, which she refers to as "fantastic" and has increased her circle of friends. Angie plays tennis one or two times per week, bike rides, takes a women's self defense class, and walks two or three miles per day.

Additionally, Angie underwent six weeks of individual counseling after her neck healed. Her strong spiritual base was also a major factor in her recovery. Angie reported making the best of each moment and doesn't worry about the future. She stated, "We don't know what the future holds anyway, do we?"

*** * * * * * * * * * ***

MIMI

Mimi was a forty six year old female, wife, and mother of three children. She worked at a convenience store in 1973, where she fell victim to armed robbery and assault. Soon after the event, she retreated into a shell and developed a serious panic disorder.

Mimi remained indoors for the most part. She only went out of the house while accompanied by another adult or her children.

Through the years following the robbery and assault, Mimi went through many conventional and/or traditional counseling sessions. She did not drive a car by herself. Her home was the only place she felt safe.

In 1990, Mimi developed breast cancer and, all alone, went through much suffering. From this experience, she decided she would never be a "victim" again. From the time of the burglary she had worked at home to earn an income. However, she had never worked outside the home since that incident in 1973.

Mimi went to work for Dr. David Hoover in a neighboring city, Ft. Worth. Her family drove her to and from work. Eventually, she had the nerve to tell Dr. Hoover of her plight... her anxiety and panic attacks. He told her of a new technique that could help her to overcome her fears.

Mimi agreed to give it a try. Dr. Hoover discovered the emotion of "anger" at being a victim as a result of the robbery and assault. This emotion was stored in the liver meridian access point. Working with her for almost two hours, he discharged that NEC, as well as many others attached to this event. There was "paralyzed will" localized in the kidney meridian access point, "vulnerable" in the adrenal meridian access point, and "lost" in the heart meridian access point.

Mimi was amazed that in such a short time, Dr. Hoover unraveled what she had been tied up in knots about for twenty one

years! Within one week after the treatment, she drove herself to work alone. Her daughter bought her a car, and she began her new journey. At first, she drove only a few blocks near her home. Eventually, she became comfortable enough to go anywhere in her small town alone.

Mimi enrolled in a nursing class with her youngest daughter. She has gone on to do many other things, amazing both herself and her family. Mimi says:

> ***"The power of NET and NEAT is a very life changing process... and (it works) in a very short period of time."***

For years, Mimi was ruled, controlled, and dominated by that one event of violence so many years earlier. Now she was free of it all, thanks to Dr. Hoover and NEAT!

*** * * * * * * * * * ***

SAMANTHA

Samantha, a forty year old woman, came to see Dr. Howard Cohn for neck pain and assistance with weight reduction. She tried over tweny different diets, read many books on weight loss, went to

many counselors and therapists, followed countless exercise regimens, yet was still unable to release any weight.

Dr. Cohn discovered in first addressing her neck pain that there was a Neuro Emotional Component relating to her thyroid that was affecting her metabolic rate. The NEC was revealed as "paranoia" about being thin and slender.

Dr. Cohn traced her story back to age sixteen. She had never had a weight problem prior to that age. At sixteen, she was date raped, and her body system associated that traumatic event with being thin and attractive.

Samantha knew another girl who was thin and had also been date raped. None of her obese friends ever had anything like that happen to them. Her system imprinted that, no matter how illogical it was, if she remained obese, she would never again be raped. It was not safe to be thin in her "emotional reality." Using NEAT, Dr. Cohn cleared the NECs of "paranoia" in the thyroid meridian access point, "anger" in the liver meridian access point, and "low self-esteem" in the pancreas meridian access point.

The nerve plexuses of the lower neck supply the thyroid. When Dr. Cohn discharged the NEC in the thyroid meridian access point, both her neck pain and weight began to disappear. In a six month period, Samantha released forty two pounds.

* * * * * * * * * * *

This last case is rather lengthy and detailed, yet very powerful. It warrants reporting in detail in order to note the profound merit, value, and healing properties of NEAT. The joint efforts of their respective healing arts are clearly a role model for us all.

* * * * * * * * * * *

ABIGAIL

BACKGROUND

Abigail was a thirty eight year old, single, Caucasian female who was referred to IN-GLO Christian Counseling Center in Maryland Heights, Missouri. She suffered from Acute Stress Disorder and Post Traumatic Stress Disorder, which were manifested in extreme panic attacks.

Her first appointment was September 7, 1993. At that time, she lived in Evansville, Indiana and counseling was designated every three weeks. Between the first session and June 24, 1995, Abigail attended seventeen sessions with her psychologist, Philip Popejoy, Ph.D., L.P.C.

Abigail's treatment progressed satisfactorily, even though viewed as a long term process. Dr. Popejoy learned, through an associate, of a new procedure called Neuro Emotional Technique. He referred Abigail to Dr. James Murphy, a NET/NEAT practitioner. Dr. Murphy and he co-treated Abigail, and the effect was astonishing.

HISTORY

Abigail experienced physical and sexual abuse from a very early age. The impact of her abuse led to a lifetime of victimization. As an adult, Abigail was raped, abused, and party to both hetero and homosexual relationships.

Sexual abuse as a child involved incestous rape by her father. Her father, an alcoholic, also allowed his associates to rape Abigail on an ongoing basis. Several times, Abigail was gang raped by her father and his friends.

The activity of Abigail's father became occultic in nature, and the sexual abuse turned ritualistic. During these rituals, Abigail found herself responsible for the torture and death of small animals. The punishment was always sexual and incredibly painful.

Abigail's father's group graduated into the torture of other children. Abigail was always made to feel responsible for anyone else being hurt. Eventually, Abigail, as a small child of four to five years old, was forced to participate in the murder of another child. Abigail felt totally responsible for the death of that child! Due to the associated guilt feelings, she would not protect herself from the sexual assaults of others.

In order to emotionally survive, she suppressed all memory of her early life. Her later life experience, however, seemed to re-enact the same process of personal destruction.

Abigail was very involved in the Roman Catholic Church, being drawn, specifically, to the sacraments of the church. She was repeatedly attacked in her religious search during her early adulthood.

Once, while on a visit to the Vatican in Rome, Italy, Abigail was sexually assaulted. The assault took place in the Vatican where she was well within crying (sound) distance of several people who could have come to her aid. However, Abigail shut down and as hard as she tried, she could not resist or cry out for help. She was "frozen" in the trauma of the drama.

Abigail's relationships, both heterosexual and homosexual, were all abusive or neglectful in nature. Many of them had occultic overtones. For a short period of time, she was romantically involved with a male "white" witch.

Meanwhile, Abigail's work environment continued to be abusive. A series of doctors abused Abigail verbally and effectively destroyed her self confidence.

Abigail attended spiritual retreats for victims of abuse. She also attended an interdenominational church which provided her with very strong emotional support, yet continued with the Catholic Church.

Abigail suffered from binge eating, insomnia, lost time, unspecified feelings of dread, and paranoia. She had problems relating to family, work, and friends. Additionally, at the end of 1994, Abigail was diagnosed with Dissociative Identity Disorder. By the end of June, 1995, her problems relating to family, work, and friends improved.

During the course of counseling, Abigail's condition improved considerably. She was able to remove herself from an abusive work environment and establish boundaries before accepting a new position. The doctors in her present position have praised her work consistently and kept the emotional boundaries which she established.

The greatest area of the remaining difficulty consisted of the past abuse issues related to her family. Abigail had a generally positive relationship with her siblings, but a great deal of difficulty with her mother.

Abigail's mother was a manipulating and controlling woman who had a vested interest to staying in denial. Abigail's progress was sabotaged by her mother every step of the way. Because of her post traumatic issues and her issues with her mother, Abigail's overall functioning still contained serious symptoms.

As Abigail explored the extreme physical and sexual abuse of her father, the memories emerged during weekend retreats. She had very bizarre and disturbing dreams and remembered being tied to a large tree in front of her house. Several people were involved in a ceremony in which she was dedicated to Satan.

Abigail had always felt that she was "evil" and could not understand why. This memory began to help her understand why she could never shake this feeling of being evil.

Her counseling involved some reality testing to ensure that her memories were not symbolic. Abigail, her psychologist, Dr. Popejoy, and a female associate visited the house where she was raised. Her family no longer lived there. Dr. Popejoy obtained permission to walk the grounds.

Abigail found the tree to which she had been tied. This tree was located in such a way that she could see the house, yet still be hidden.

Abigail had a memory of a creek which ran sideways across the hill, which made no sense to her. They discovered that the property had a manmade pond with runoff directed to a drainage ditch that ran parallel to the house. Dr. Popejoy questioned the current owner about the direction of the water flow. The owner responded by saying the direction was sideways in order to reduce erosion. He also told them that when his family purchased the property, the drainage ditch resembled a creek due to the amount of plant growth.

With this validation, Abigail and Dr. Popejoy were able to firm up her memories, as well, and bring closure to this particular memory. After that session, she felt overwhelmed by what she had remembered and decided to take some time off from counseling.

When Abigail re-entered counseling in November, 1994, three sessions were intended to evaluate her progress. Abigail was not as anxious as when she first entered counseling. However, she was having difficulty handling stress in all facets of her relationships.

The session in the woods had helped her realize that her feelings were based on actual memories. She still, however, could not shake the feeling of being evil. The memory of being forced to participate in the ritual killing of the small child continued to be overwhelming. Abigail became aware of losing time and that there were "other people" operating inside her.

The last two sessions of 1994 dealt with the memory of the little girl's murder. Abigail remembered a knife being placed in her hand. A man (she could not see his face) placed his hand over hers and forced her to impale the child. Abigail felt like a murderer! Again, Dr. Popejoy used reality testing to help her understand that she had no choice in the matter.

Through guided imagery, he helped her take the knife out of the little girl Abigail's hands. In a religious ceremony, they reclaimed

the dead child in the name of Jesus Christ and prayed for angels to take the child into heaven. Although this was a healing session for Abigail, she still felt empty inside. It was as if her body did not belong to her. A remnant of responsibility for the child's death remained.

Abigail's overall functioning level improved. She was working for a group of doctors who appreciated her abilities. She was working on building healthy boundaries with her mom. The most pressing issue that faced Abigail at the end of 1994 was her uncertainty about her sexuality.

Dr. Popejoy had six counseling goals for 1995. They were:

To free Abigail from feeling responsible for the child's murder.

To help Abigail realize that she was a competent professional.

To help Abigail regain a normal sleep pattern.

To help Abigail overcome her binge eating.

To establish firm boundaries with her mother.

To clarify her sexuality.

By the end of the first half of 1995, Abigail made definite progress on all six goals. This was a very difficult time for her personally, but she was determined to heal.

The murder of the child was still the most painful part of her counseling. She could not let go of the shame, guilt, and sorrow over the child's death. Abigail believed that the child was with God and was safe, yet recognized that her personality had fractures. Her alter child personalities still felt the pain and responsibility for the child's death.

Much of Abigail's post traumatic stress eased as she worked through the stress of this memory. Abigail and Dr. Popejoy realized that while progress was being made, it would be several years before Abigail would truly be healed from this memory.

The second goal for 1995 was accomplished through reality testing. Abigail received a very positive evaluation from her employer. The evaluation was outstanding in every category. She found it difficult to believe the evaluation, but could not deny the employer's positive written statements. When Abigail contemplated quitting, her employer practically begged her to stay!

She became an integral member of a surgical team specializing in organ transplants. Abigail participated in several life-giving operations, which helped balance her memories and boost her ego strength.

Her sleep and eating difficulties showed sporadic improvement. During times of low stress, she made solid improvement. However, improvement was marginal at times of stress.

In 1995, Abigail began mending the relationship with her mother with renewed energy. She became aware of when and how her mother controlled and manipulated her.

One way in which her mother manipulated her was to buy Abigail clothing two sizes too small. When Abigail brought this to her attention, her mother would say, "I guess I can't do anything right."

In the past, Abigail rescued her, wanting her not to feel bad. This issue became more intense in June, 1995 because Abigail planned to attend a family reunion (her mother also attended) around the fourth of July.

Abigail's sexuality was a major obstacle. Her sexual relationships with men tended to be abusive, while her relationships with women were satisfying. She had female friends, as well as male friends. She feared crossing the line and thereby damaging any of her friendships.

Counseling centered on contacting Abigail's alter personalities. Femininity was considered, by her alter personalities, to be very dangerous because it led to abuse! Therefore, this made Abigail feel very uncomfortable when she was feminine.

In June, 1995, she began to work with Dr. Jim Murphy of Mexico, Missouri as an adjunct to counseling. Dr. Murphy would use NET or NEAT either the day before or after the counseling session.

He discovered Abigail had symptoms of fibromyalgia, weight gain, paranoia, anxiety, insomnia, nightmares, claustrophobia, severe depression, work-a-holism, rheumatism in most all joints of the body, and leg aches. Abigail told Dr. Murphy that she wanted to discontinue the use of non-steroidal anti-inflammatory drugs, to regain her ability to sleep nights, to have an end to the nightmares, and to become depression free.

FINDINGS AND TREATMENT

Dr. Murphy began immediately, noting that her system required the NEAT first. It was as if the emotions were just ready to "pop up" and "be cleared."

He discovered that the most significant NECs were localized in the uterus meridian access point (MAP) of "vivid dreaming." "Abandoned" and "deserted" were encountered in the small intestine MAP. In the stomach MAP, "low self-esteem" and "obsession" were located in the spleen MAP. "Crying," "sadness," and "grief" were located in the lung MAP. Next, "anger" in the liver MAP and "grief" in the right lung MAP were cleared... all in that order...all imprinted during those early childhood traumas.

Next, Dr. Murphy asked Abigail to create her own life with personal declarative statements. She came up with fifty to sixty. A brief overview of some of those are:

"I'm OKAY with being a child of God."

"I'm OKAY with believing God created me."

"It is OKAY to be a woman and not be raped."

"I am OKAY without hiding in body fat."

"I am OKAY with looking at difficult situations of issues."

"I am OKAY with being sexual."

"I am OKAY with my heart being attractive."

"I believe it is OKAY to feel."

During the following six months, Dr. Murphy prescribed three homeopathic NET remedies to assist in the healing process. These included "*Earth*" for the stomach meridian, emotions of "low self-esteem" and "obsession"; "*Fire*" for the small intestine, emotions of "abandoned" and "deserted"; and "*Wood*" for the liver, emotion of "anger."

Dr. Murphy checked Abigail's congruence with additional statements, including:

"I Am."

"I am a Being."

"I exist."

"I am a woman."

Abigail had NECs around all of these. He also checked her on "The Personal Bill of Rights" from the Twelve Step Program. Some of the statements that tested positive were:

> **"I can take care of myself no matter what."**
>
> **"I have the right to change and to expect honesty from others."**
>
> **"I have the right to change and grow."**
>
> **"I can be healthier than those around me."**
>
> **"I have a right to all my feelings."**
>
> **"I have a right to discover and know my child within."**
>
> **"I have a right to grieve over actual or threatened losses."**

Many more NECs were discovered, discharged, and cleared by Dr. Murphy.

RESULTS

The results were remarkable! The post traumatic stress symptoms disappeared within two months of beginning the NET and NEAT! Abigail was able to leave the counseling process in October, 1995. It was Dr. Popejoy's opinion that without NET, Abigail would have been in counseling for at least three more years.

October is a very difficult month for victims of ritual abuse. Abigail reported no difficulty at Halloween.

Several other stressors occurred between July and October 1995 which, in the past, would have destroyed any progress she made. Four people that she knew died in August, including the suicide of a pastor. In September, an elderly friend died.

In September, Abigail also attended a spiritual retreat where the nun was emotionally abusive in her teaching methodology. In the past, Abigail would have been devastated! During this retreat, however, she was merely irritated.

Abigail went to a family reunion and dealt successfully with others' attempts to sabotage her. She dealt with her mother without dissociating. She released herself from responsibility for the murder of the child in less than one month after the first NEAT treatment.

Abigail has not used non-steroidal anti-inflammatory drugs for five months. Her eating habits have improved, her weight has decreased, and she is much less jumpy. She can maintain eye contact and does not feel the need to wear sunglasses as she did previously.

Abigail now eats in the employee cafeteria (previously she associated the cafeteria with the Vatican) and tolerates being in a crowded elevator.

Her nightmares have subsided, and she sleeps soundly. Dr. Popejoy stated that all six goals of the counseling were sufficiently satisfied for Abigail to function in a healthy manner.

Abigail described her experience with NEAT and Dr. Murphy by stating:

> **"After my first session with Dr. Murphy using NEAT, the following session with Dr. Popejoy was the most significant session we had had in two years. It was an incredible release! I feel that Dr. Murphy, in using NEAT, has stretched me on the inside. The effect of NEAT for me has been dramatic. In many areas, I feel that I have been able to let go. I feel that I have been able to integrate the past with my present life."**

Dr. Murphy continues to see Abigail once every three weeks on the average. He stresses the need for checkups and continued growth type care.

In reviewing, reporting, and contemplating the pain, misery, and dis-ease imposed upon little Abigail, created by one so lost, so in fear... and then of Abigail, the woman, healing, I am reminded of an old favorite hymn:

> ***"Amazing Grace, how sweet the sound,***
> ***That saved a wretch like me.***
> ***I once was lost, but now am found...***
> ***Was blind, but now I see!"***

How unfortunate that Abigail's father's experiences, his learning, and his resultant choices led him into such destructive behavior... and that he forgot this Grace and who he *really* was!

* * * * * * * * * * *

POSTSCRIPT

ALPHA - THE BEGINNING

The theme of this book has been about *healing*... about *hope*, about *faith*, and about *love*. The recognition of the negative forces within us creates the first step in their healing. Our efforts will hopefully be applied to mend the damage rather than to forms of retaliatory destructiveness. Martin Luther once said:

> ***"Everything that is done in the world is done by hope. No husbandman would sow one grain of corn if he hoped not it would grow up and become seed; no bachelor would marry a wife if he hoped not to have children; no merchant or tradesman would set himself to work if he did not reap benefit thereby."***

Hope is an awareness of a realizable wish. Hope springs forth eternally. Hope looks forward. Faith is believing without proof. Faith is trust. Faith is constancy. Rudolph Bultmann, philosopher, theologian, and teacher, in his esteemed paper, *Leap of Faith*, describes the challenge of humanity's forward soul journey. He speaks of the "leap into the void," to trust when there is no third dimensional evidence upon which to base trust.

Paul Tillich, in *Dynamics of Faith*, defines the dynamics of faith as the dynamics of humanity's "ultimate concern." In the Bible, we have a wonderful illustration of this, relating to the three kings who were in the desert, without water for their men or their horses. They consulted the prophet, Elisha, who gave them these words of wisdom:

> **"Thus saith the Lord... Ye shall not see wind, neither shall ye see rain, yet make this valley full of ditches."**

We must prepare for the thing we have asked for, when there isn't the smallest sign of it in sight!

> ***"Faith knows it has already received and acts accordingly. My faith is built upon a rock, and my heart's desire now comes to pass, under grace in a miraculous way. I am poised and powerful, my greatest expectations are realized***

in a miraculous way. I water my wilderness with faith and suddenly it blossoms as a rose. I know there is nothing to defeat God, therefore, there is nothing to defeat me. I now exercise my fearless faith in three ways... by thinking, speaking, and acting. Before I called I was answered and I now gather in my harvest in a remarkable way."

Your Word is Your Wand
~ Florence Shinn, 1928

The antithesis of Love is not hate, as is most commonly thought. The antithesis of Love is fear. As Franklin Delano Roosevelt once said, "We have nothing to fear but fear itself!" At his 1994 Inaugural Speech, Nelson Mandela spoke these very powerful words:

"Our deepest fear is not that we are inadequate. Our deepest fear is that we are powerful beyond measure. It is our light, not our darkness, that most frightens us. We ask ourselves, who am I to be brilliant, gorgeous, talented, and fabulous? Actually, who are you not to be? You are a child of God. Your playing small doesn't serve the world. There is nothing enlightened about

shrinking so that other people won't feel insecure around you. We are born to make manifest the glory of God within us. It's not just in some of us; it's in everyone. And as we let our own light shine, we unconsciously give other people permission to do the same. As we are liberated from our own fear, our presence automatically liberates others."

To let go, to release fear, is an ultimate act of love. To do so takes willingness, determination, faith, and hope.

Ouspensky states in "*Tertium Organum*" that "love is a cosmic phenomenon" which opens us to the fourth dimensional world, "The World of the Wondrous." Love is God in manifestation, the strongest force in the universe.

***Real love* also recognizes and honors the Divine spark within others. In India, there is a greeting which states not "Good Morning" or "Hello" but as:**

"Nameste!
I salute the Divinity within you."

God is Love and within us all! When we release that which blocks our claiming and owning of our "Divine Blueprint," then are we *free.* This is Truth… and Truth sets us free!

Hope and faith then are implicit characteristics of Love. Plato once said, "For love is the desire of the whole, and the pursuit of the whole is called love." Many years later, Jesus taught that God is love. Basically, these have the same meaning.

It is my hope that mankind will choose to heal. It is my faith that this healing will transpire. It is my belief that we have the power to love. This will take courage and from that springs determination to speed human happiness.

"And the merging began again…
the merging into being.
And we were flying now,
higher and higher into the ethers
of all seeing and complete being.
We flew over the Earth
and there was Light,
and the Light was the calling forth of all souls.
And the people joined hands across the seas.
Their minds linked in one consciousness.
And there was no separation.
All children belonged to all people.
All marriages created union.
The death of competition became the birth of acceptance.
The greed was replaced with giving,

And the fear replaced with the memory of all kingdoms
dancing together in harmony.
And I watched the feet of the people light upon the Earth.
They brought flowers to celebrate their joining
with the Earth... the heavens... and each other.
For there was no separation.
They truly remembered.
And in that moment, we were all one.
And there was no time,
and I died and was reborn.
And the memory was light
And I flew home."

I Remember Union
~ Flo Aeveia Magdalena

I close this section of the book with a quote from a beloved sister, a patient who exemplifies faith, hope, and love in very extraordinary ways. She writes:

"I feel deep and heartfelt appreciation for the powerful and positive impact of NEAT on my life. NEAT continues to give me hope, support, and assistance in my efforts to heal and grow. With laser accuracy, it helps me target,

release, and heal emotional blocks lodged deep within me. I experience (with great joy!) pockets of grief, loss, and abandonment losing their grip and control over my life. My relationships, health, work, and even my dreams are transforming in very positive ways. I know without a doubt NEAT helps me. It is a blessing as I unearth the wondrous 'Being' that lies within."

~ Julie Paige

This is not an ending. There are no real endings. There are only beginnings... but of course, with the *gift* of Free Will, that is a choice. A choice, a decision to be made by one and all.

Nameste... I salute the Divinity within you!

* * * * * * * * * * *

THE O.N.E. FOUNDATION
(OUR NET EFFECT)

* * * * * * * * * * *

The O.N.E. Foundation is a worldwide interdisciplinary health research, educational, and service foundation that has been established through the dreams and vision of Dr. Scott Walker, Dr. Debra Walker, and other dedicated NET/NEAT doctors who know and have experienced the powerful healing properties of this technique. THE O.N.E FOUNDATION stands for "Our Net Effect."

Incorporated in 1993, The O.N.E. Foundation is under the trusteeship of Dr. Scott Walker. It is a global, nonprofit, interdisciplinary research and educational organization made up of health professionals and others who are dedicated to promoting world health by utilizing the Neuro Emotional Technique and Neuro Emotional Anti-sabotage Techniques.

The O.N.E. Foundation represents the deep desire to have a powerful impact on the world's health by demonstrating the efficacy of NET/NEAT through clinical trials and peer review processes. It distributes publications which support individual NET/NEAT practitioners and their patients.

Much research and funding for that research is needed! This is O.N.E. way to Save the World. You can be a part of this very vital Foundation and its projects!

The Board of Directors of the Foundation invites you to join and support this dynamic organization. For your opportunity to make a world of difference, for NET/NEAT doctor referral lines, and for information, call:

1-800-638-1411 or 1-619-944-1030

* * * * * * * * * * *

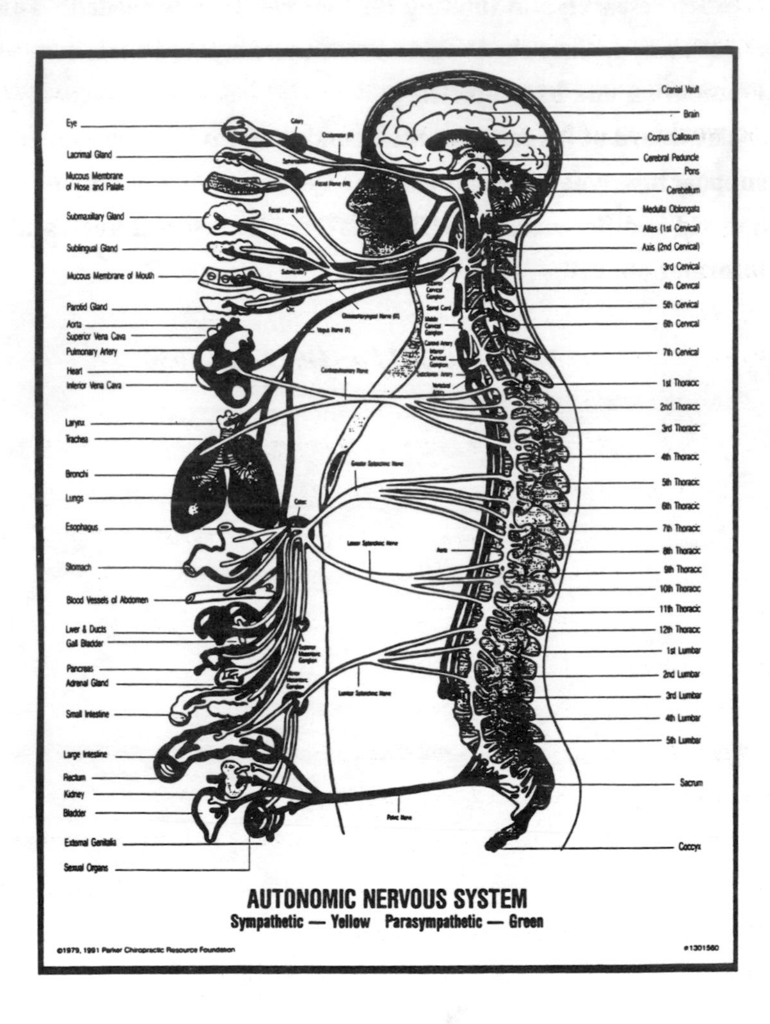

AUTONOMIC NERVOUS SYSTEM

Sympathetic — Yellow Parasympathetic — Green

The historical background, philosophy, and technical perspectives of NEAT/NET are herein provided. Hopefully, these Addendums will further clarify and create better understanding of the workings of NEAT and NET.

ADDENDUM #1

THE INTERCONNECTION OF ALL BODY SYSTEMS

"The real source of knowledge is within; the world outside only gives you facts to relate to that particular knowledge that is already within you."

~ Swami Rama

Homo Sapiens are indeed whole beings with multiple parts. These parts are interrelated and communicate through very complex and sophisticated systems.

The human body, which has many parts, is a unity, and these parts, despite their multiplicity, constitute one single body. So it is that one might say, all our parts (or quadrants) are interrelated and cannot help but interface and affect the others.

Since the days of Rene' Descarte (1596-1650) and Isaac Newton (1642-1727), modern medicine has attempted to separate the physical body from the mental body. Descarte, French philosopher and mathematician, believed that the body and mind are distinct and separate. He further believed that they should be treated as such.

In spite of the growing volumes of research and scientific data to the contrary, many psychologists and psychiatrists cling to the belief that the emotional ills of their patients are sourced only in the brain.

We see, therefore, the continuation of the terms "mental illness" and "mental disease." A talk-and-reason-it-out therapeutic process is utilized by more clinicians today. In addition, the prescribing of psychiatric drugs is at an alarming all time high!

Dr. Peter Breggan, in his courageous, searing, myth shattering book *Toxic Psychiatry* shows how dangerous, even potentially brain-damaging, many of the drugs, electric shock, and other treatments have become to psychiatric patients.

Breggan provides serious evidence that the pharmaceutical companies provide the backbone of financial support for the American Psychiatry Association. He further states that there has been a betrayal of the most fundamental essence of what it means to be human by those within the medical community, especially in the field of psychiatry.

Instead of drugs, we must address the psycho-spiritual aspects of the patient through love, kindness, understanding, and moral support in order to obtain true healing. This concept is not new, but is an eternal truth. We must reconnect the body systems with honor, respect, balance, and homeostasis.

Blair Justice, Ph.D., Professor of Psychology at the University of Texas Health Science Center in Houston, Texas has co-authored with Rita Justice, Ph.D., a book entitled *The Abusing Family, Violence in the City*. They state that few "can keep up with the mushrooming research (from the molecular to the behavioral) that generates new findings almost daily on the profound effect of the brain on the body." In another of his books, *Who Gets Sick*, he states:

> **"Unraveling some of the chemistry of thinking is helping to build the foundation of an exciting new field of molecular psychology, which is devoted to probing the interaction between chemical molecules in the brain and our cognitions and behavior."**

In *Behavioral Medicine Abstracts*, S.M. Levy so closely links the brain, nervous system, immune system, and endocrine system that they constitute a single regulatory network in the body. We can no

longer intelligently hold the "separatist" concept of the body's makeup.

THE FOUR QUADRANTS OF THE HUMAN SYSTEM

Elizabeth Kubler-Ross, M.D., is the world renowned pioneer on the grieving process. Her book *On Death and Dying* forever transformed the understanding and therapeutic processing of professionals caring for those suffering from loss. When speaking at a conference, she once said:

> **"When we try to conceptualize what human beings are all about, we always share that they really consist of four quadrants:**
>
> **1) the physical quadrant,**
>
> **2) the emotional quadrant,**
>
> **3) the intellectual quadrant,**
> **(which is very hypertrophic, overly emphasized, or utilized in too many people), and**
>
> **4) the spiritual quadrant."**

She continued by saying:

"And if you want to become whole, and I really mean whole... when you are whole, you are at total peace, you have no more anxiety, you can accept your fellow man where they are, and you are at total balance and harmony between the four quadrants."

These quadrants (bodies within the body) must all be interrelated, as they comprise a system that is a *unit*. Whatever happens to one quadrant also affects the other three.

Ernest L. Ross, Ph.D., researcher, and David B. Cheek, M.D., Ob/Gyn, in their book *Mind-Body Therapy*, explore the integration of information substances, their receptors, and a classic technique of mind-body healing.

They identify this as the "ideo-dynamic approach." They carefully outline the new models of psycho-neuro-immunology, psycho-biology, and stress related psychosomatic disorders. The authors illustrate the major pathways of mind-body communication and healing with hundreds of engaging case reports from forty years of Dr. Cheek's clinical work.

From centuries ago, one author writes:

"The human body, which has many parts, is a unity, and those parts, despite their multiplicity, constitute one single body. The body is not one member, but many.

If the foot should say, 'Because I am not a hand, I don't belong to the body,' does that alter the fact that the foot IS a part of the body? Or if the ear should say, 'Because I am not an eye, I don't belong to the body,' does that mean that the ear is not part of the body? After all, if the body were all one eye, for example, where would be the sense of hearing? Or if it were all one ear, where would be the sense of smell? For if everything were concentrated in one part, how could there be a body at all?

The fact is there are many parts, but only one body. or that the eye cannot say to the hand, 'I don't need you!' or, again can the head say to the feet, 'I don't need you!" On the contrary, those parts of the body which have obvious function are the more essential to health; and to those parts of the body which seem to us to be less deserving of notice, we have to allow the highest honor or function.

The parts which do not look beautiful have a deeper beauty in the work they do, while parts which look beautiful may not be at all essential to life!

But God has harmonized the whole body by giving importance of function to the parts which lack apparent importance, that the body should work together as a whole with all the members in sympathetic relationship with one

another.

So it happens that if one member suffers, all other members suffer with it, and if one member is honored, all the members share a common joy."

The New Testament in Modern English
~ Saint Paul, Chapter 12

So, when we remember the stumped toe, the toothache, or the migraine headache we have experienced, do we also not remember that the entire system (body) suffered, including our mood and the changes in how we related to others? And how our performance on the job was less effective, and perhaps how our relationships were affected?

For centuries, the Orientals have known about the interconnectedness and intricacies of the human body. Acupuncture, based on the meridian access reflex points of the body, has been utilized for centuries in health care for multiple physiological disorders, assistance, treatment, pain relief, and balancing the body's energy system.

In recent years, western civilization has begun to incorporate the philosophy of this ancient wisdom. It is often utilized in the form of acupressure (applying pressure to the meridian reflex points, either manually or with instruments).

Affirming the value of acupressure, a recent double blind research project was completed by Terry Oleson, Ph.D. and William Flocco. The results of this project were published in the *Obstetrics and Gynecology Journal* in December, 1993.

In their study, acupressure was applied to the specific related reflex points of the feet and hands to study the effects on women suffering from Premenstrual Syndrome (PMS).

The results were positive. Those women who received the acupressure on meridian reflex points connected to the reproductive and endocrine systems experienced improvement. PMS symptoms were reduced.

THE GERM THEORY

The germ theory has been the cornerstone of the medical model. The concept of the bio-psycho-social risk factor of disease is a noticeable departure from the germ theory. Dr. Justice, in *Who Gets Sick*, writes:

> ***"Although medicine no longer attempts to explain all illness in terms of a specific micro-organism for every disease, its model still suggests that pathology is largely caused by foreign forces that invade our bodies and damage our organs."***

He goes on to say:

> ***"Under the newer concept of disease, tissue damage is seen as more the results normal bodily processes gone awry or disputed than it is the dirty work of microbes or other external culprits. These processes include the activity of the neurotransmitters in our brain cells, the stress hormones of our endocrine glands and nervous systems, and suppressor cells of our immune functioning. When imbalances occur in these processes, pathology often results."***

Dr. Deepak Chopra, respected endocrinologist, is the author of *Ageless Body, Timeless Mind.* He returned to his native India to explore Ayurveda, humanity's most ancient healing tradition.

Dr. Chopra was puzzled as he observed patients in his own practice completely recover after being given only a few months to live. In his own evocative and extraordinary way, he has brought together current research in Western medicine, physics, and neuroscience. Armed with the insights of Ayurvedic theory, he notes that the human system is controlled by a "*network of intelligence.*" He states:

> ***"The first thing that is killed in the laboratory is the***

delicate web of intelligence that binds the body together. When a blood cell rushes to a wound site and begins to form a clot, it has not traveled there at random. It actually knows where to go and what to do when it gets there, as surely as a paramedic…in fact, more surely, since it acts completely spontaneously and without guesswork."

Dr. Chopra continues in stating:

"The body, we must admit, has a mind of its own."

This is a mysterious aspect of our basic nature. It is one in which, through the experience of NEAT, one begins an amazing journey into awe and trust of the wisdom of the human organism.

Dr. Chopra reveals to us in his *"Escaping the Prison of the Intellect"* cassette tape, how the intellectual creates prisoners of us. It mistakenly creates images of reality for reality itself. As we are trapped in this suffocating web, we lose our freedom.

As Dr. Elizabeth Kubler-Ross states, we are "hypertrophic or excessively developed in the mental quadrant." This is but another way of painting the picture of this imbalance and imprisonment.

We *can* escape this prison. We *can* come to our true nature and experience *unbounded freedom* via the process of NEAT and NET.

This is not to say that there are no other paths in which to accomplish this freedom. It is only to say that NET/NEAT is a thorough, rapid avenue for the human organism to reclaim its power and the true nature of itself.

STRESS, EMOTIONS, AND THE HUMAN RESPONSE

Most of us are aware of the modern research which indicated the damaging effects of stress on the human organism. However, we postulate that it is not the stress itself, but the way in which we respond to what happens to us in life. It is that response which makes the difference in health or illness.

Hans B. Selye spent fifty years researching stress. In his book *Stress of Life*, he came to the conclusion in 1976 that it is not stress itself, but the *way* in which we *react* to the stress that is significant. The focus is then shifted from the stress (outward) itself to how we cope (inward) with it. Here is an example:

> While driving through heavy traffic, a fellow driver becomes impatient with another driver. He perceives this driver to be slowing him down. He repeatedly honks his horn, screeches around him, yells obscenities, perhaps shakes a fist at him, or worse.

Now, the other driver has choices. He can,

1) **fight back verbally or otherwise,**
2) **report him to the police,**
3) **dismiss him and ignore the incident, or**
4) **find humor in the guy being in such a rush and getting so upset.**

Selye says, about individual reactions to stress:

> ***"The first choice will discharge adrenaline that increases blood pressure and pulse rate, the whole nervous system becomes alarmed and tense in anticipation of combat."***

Perhaps the second choice does not register any physiological changes and more likely, the third choice would probably register none. Whereas the fourth choice might even stimulate the system positively, such as elevate the beta-endorphins, stimulate seratonin production, and so forth.

Now, if one happens to be a coronary candidate, this first choice reaction could precipitate a heart attack. What then caused death? The insults? Traffic? No, Selye would say it was his *REACTION* to the stress surrounding the situation. It is the way in which he experienced the stress.

Perhaps we are now met with the objection of many who would say:

> ***"But there are times and situations in which I cannot stop my reactions to certain situations! There are other times I wish I could react or respond in positive or constructive ways. Try as I might, I cannot bring myself to do so!"***

This is a very common expression in our "victim oriented" society. One does not have to accept a victim's role. ***There are ways to reclaim control and power in one's life.***

THE SHIFTING CONSCIOUSNESS

Volumes more data could be referenced in the discussion of the Mind-Body Connection concept. Drs. Carl Simonton, Bernie Siegel, Larry Dossey, Deepak Chopra, Stephen Locke, Norman Shealey, and countless others in the medical field have been baffled by their exceptional patients.

These doctors have watched as their patients lived much longer than expected or even became completely free of so-called "terminal" illnesses. As a result, they learned much from these patients.

They began their search, their own personal journey, questioning the traditional medical model, and collectively, have offered volumes of creative thought, research, data, techniques, hope, and wisdom. They are moving toward a NEW MODEL.

Here is where the NET/NEAT enters. This book is primarily a presentation of case histories of those who have experienced the NET/ NEAT process. As a result, they have found themselves in touch with, and utilizing, their own resources.

While perhaps the NEAT/NET patient still "does not like their life circumstances" they are now more able to observe and experience themselves responding differently to those same situations.

Their personal histories do not appear to change, yet most individuals experience a shift in their "life circumstances" eventually. They experience empowerment to "change those things they can change," and, in "serenity," let the rest go.

The wisdom of the following proverb paints us a beautiful picture of this serenity.

> ***"If there is light in the soul,***
> ***There will be beauty in the person.***
> ***If there is beauty in the person,***
> ***There will be harmony in the house.***
> ***If there is harmony in the house,***

There will be order in the nation.
If there is order in the nation,
There will be peace in the world."

~ Chinese Proverb

* * * * * * * * * *

ADDENDUM #2

THE TRIANGLE OF HEALTH
AND
THE HOME RUN FORMULA

An idea whose time has come is a powerful thing. In 1985, D.D. Palmer, the founder of Chiropractic, said:

> **"The determining causes of disease are traumatism, poison, and auto-suggestion."**

While D.D. Palmer's language is perhaps archaic for today, one hundred years later Dr. Scott Walker has modernized the language. Dr. Walker utilizes the graphic triangle in a format to emphasize the truth of Palmer's principle. This graphic is referred to as:

"THE TRIANGLE OF HEALTH"

Dr. Walker explains:

> **EACH EQUILATERAL SIDE OF THE TRIANGLE REPRESENTS ASPECTS OF THOSE FACTORS AFFECTING MAN'S HEALTH. ONE SIDE IS STRUCTURAL (TRAUMATISM), THE SECOND SIDE IS BIOCHEMICAL (POISON), AND THE THIRD, EMOTIONAL (AUTO-SUGGESTION).**

He further states:

"Our three-sided model suggests that one-third of the causative factors in disease are, in fact EMOTIONALLY RELATED."

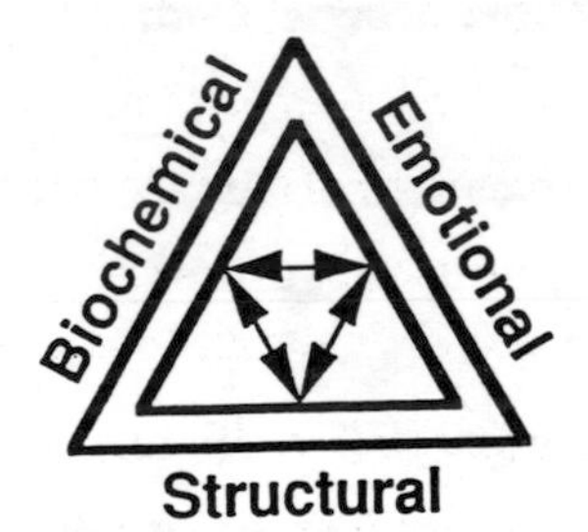

"The determining causes of Disease are Traumatism, Poison, & Autosuggestion."

---D.D. Palmer pg.359 The Chiropractor's Adjuster

He continues:

"To those of us who use this equilateral triangle paradigm, the implications are very significant. We are all versed in the definitive consequences of structural and biochemical stress. We are also well-schooled in the mechanics of these processes in the dysfunctional state. Emotional stress, while being a familiar term, has eluded the chiropractor as a tangibly defined, mechanically-delineated or treatable entity. Emotions, which are not in physiological harmony within the individual, are themselves a component of an easily diagnosed complex termed a neuro-emotional complex.

THE HOME RUN FORMULA

Both inspired by the Triangle of Health and recognizing the need for the modern man/woman to have added nutrition in the daily diet, Dr. Walker developed *The Home Run Formula*. This formula, if followed, provides added Clinical Success.

The Home Run Formula utilizes all four bases to hit a "home-run" for the patient's health with:

E	= *Emotions*	*via*	*Emotions (NET)*
T	= *Toxins*		*Homeopathics*

B	=	***Biochemistry***	***Nutrition***
S	=	***Structure***	***Adjustments***

To hit a home-run, the doctor must touch all four bases. Dr. Walker reveals another interpretation of the *ETBS* acronym:

E **=** ***Every***

T **=** ***Time***

B **=** ***Be***

S **=** ***Safe***

Following this philosophy, the NET doctor is keeping TABs (Touching All Bases) on his/her patients while going to bat for *them!*

Allergies are so common an ailment perhaps no one has escaped its discomforts. An example of utilizing the *Home Run Formula* in discovery and treating the patient for desensitization:

(*E*) First Base: The NET doctor would cross check the Allergy Point to the Emotional Points. If there is a positive test, the doctor would run NET to clear the NEC.

(*T*) Second Base: (Toxins) The doctor would cross check

the Allergy Point to the BMI (Body Memory Indicator, {Toxins}). If a positive test, the doctor fixes with NET Remedy #8, Allergy, possibly #11, Visceral Polarity or NET Remedies #9, ER911.

(B) **Third Base: (Biochemistry) The doctor checks the ACTIVE Allergy Point with Standard Process Antronex or Allerplex added to the mouth to see if it becomes strong. If strong, the Antronex (for acute), or Allerplex (chronic), are administered.**

(S) **Fourth Base: (Structure) The doctor would cross check the Allergy Point to the Atlas (CI). If needed from this testing, the doctor would adjust the structure.**

After finding an active Allergy Point, the doctor semantically muscle tests for the offending substance through muscle testing, using the Dr. Walker's "*ABCDE*"s.

"Something you *Ate,*
Something you *Breathed,*
Something you *Contacted,*
Something you *Drank,*
Something *Electromagnetic."*

In following these procedures on all four bases, areas contributing to health (or dis-ease) are covered and Clinical Success (Home Run) is achieved.

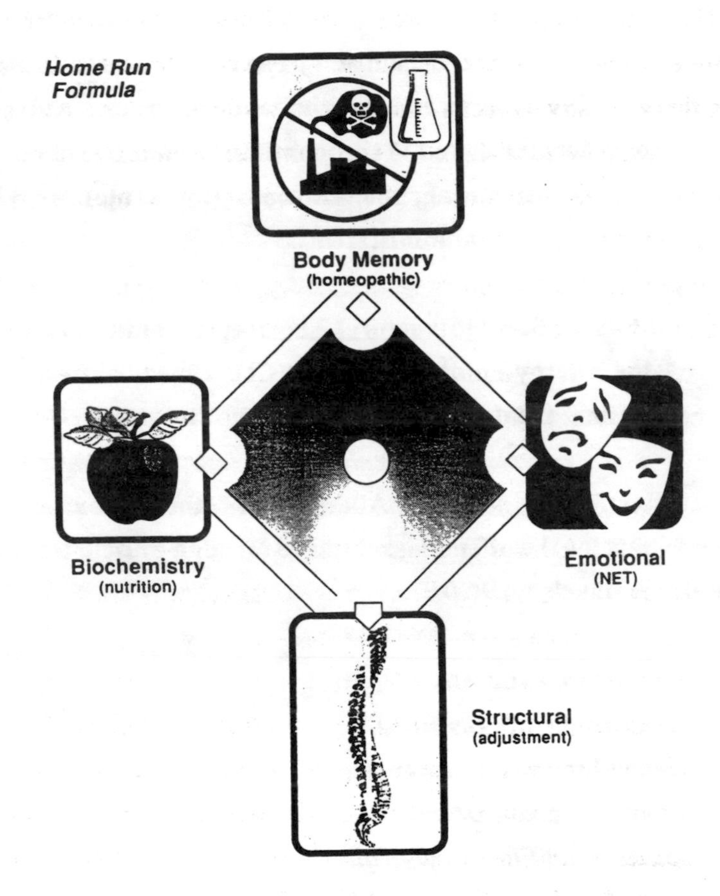

NEURO EMOTIONAL COMPLEX

Perhaps one could partially define a *Neuro Emotional Complex* (N.E.C.) as an imprint the human organism adapted to in response to some experience. Whether real or imagined, something is perceived as a threat to any aspect of its survival while in a vulnerable position or condition. Dr. Walker believes that *Neuro Emotional Complexes* are at least as common as nutritional imbalances and structural subluxations.

Imagine the human organism to be a very precise, sophisticated, and intricate computer. Everything that has ever been experienced by or happened to that unit is stored in the system somewhere on a diskette. There is the potential for existence of hundreds, more probably thousands, of these diskettes. Many of which contain *Emotional Realities*, imprinted with mild to severe traumas.

These Emotional Realities, termed *Neuro Emotional Complexes,* are cleared or discharged in much the same way that one taps the "delete" button on a computer keyboard!

A Neuro Emotional Complex is a mind/body pattern in which nerve pressure caused by a spinal mis-alignment is linked with a negative emotion. While not all emotions are linked with a spinal misalignment, in those cases where it is connected, it is termed a Neuro Emotional Complex, (NEC).

The NEC is a complex mechanism not yet fully understood. The sympathetic nervous system, in the presence of a conscious or unconscious negative emotion, may manifest a subluxation as a consequence of imbalance or disharmony. Ill health will probably result when this occurs, especially if the body is vulnerable or compromised in any way.

A Neuro Emotional Complex is "fixed' when the patient recalls the specific negative emotion and the time it first occurred. This recall engages the neuro-emotional pattern, just as a computer operator can engage a specific program on a computer screen.

The circuitry is established as follows:
simultaneously the patient

1) mentally holds an emotional memory picture,
2) the organ meridian access point in which the NEC is localized,
3) the emotional points on the forehead,
4) while the doctor adjusts the presenting vertebral spinal mis-alignments or subluxations.

The patient becomes aware of the specific negative emotion when the doctor employs muscle testing to detect muscle imbalances in conjunction with semantic reactions. There are physiological reactions to memories or words and the body reflex points. The negative emotion will then reveal itself to the patient.

It is possible for someone to have Neuro Emotional Complexes and not be aware of them. Consider the child who was bitten by an unfriendly dog. It is possible that he or she would then feel tense and apprehensive (physiological responses such as nausea and/or breaking into a "cold" sweat) around ANY dog as an adult.

It may also be that he or she may not have the slightest idea why this reaction has occurred. Spinal subluxations associated with this experience may result in increased pain and dysfunction. Neuro Emotional Complexes of this kind are quite common, even though not in the individual's conscious awareness.

VULNERABILITY AND THE N.E.C.

As stated earlier, and to emphasize once more, Neuro Emotional Complexes are imprinted when the human organism is in a vulnerable state. Two individuals could experience what would appear to be identical experiences. One will be imprinted with a Neuro Emotional Complex (N.E.C.) and the other will not.

Identical twins experience environmental and familial situations more closely than any two people in their formative years. It is quite possible for one twin to perceive an historical reality quite differently than the other.

This different "Emotional Reality" is based upon the vulnerable state of the individual at the time of the experience. Vulnerability is

determined by the weakened state of the physical, mental or emotional quadrants of the human organism at the time of the experience.

Some years ago, identical adult female twins came to see me for stress release and coping skills in dealing with their aging parents. Their father was diagnosed with Alzheimer's disease. Both parents were in nursing homes. They had to be separated and were placed in different facilities due to the advanced state of the father's Alzheimer's symptoms.

The twins were a delightful pair who obviously had come from a very loving, mutually supportive family of origin. Not long into the session, one of the twins made a rather derogatory remark about their father. The other twin retorted with, "What are you talking about? Dad was never like that!" The first twin adamantly reiterated with, "That's the way Dad was, and you know it!"

Now into a full-blown argument, these twins obviously had a very different "reality" or "truth" in their experience with their father. They could have gone on arguing indefinitely and never come to an agreement!

As maternal twins, they were as close as any human beings can experience their physical, emotional and mental environment. Yet, each had held very different emotional truths about their father!

EMOTIONAL REALITY and HISTORICAL REALITY

Emotional Reality and Historical Reality can be, and sometimes are, identical. However, they *can* be quite different, as seen in the previous case of the maternal twins. Both realities are based upon the perception of the individual's physical, emotional, mental, and spiritual state of the individual at the *time* of the experience. Another example follows:

> **Seven-year-old Susie is in the second grade. She is assessed by her teacher to be an excellent student. She completes her work consistently and successfully on time. One day, however, she is not feeling well physically. Her head aches and her tummy hurts. She is not aware that she is feverish and coming down with the flu. She has a hard time concentrating on her work assignments. She finally finishes and turns in her paper as the recess bell rings.**
>
> **During recess, her best friend comes to her and states that she is not going to play with her today. She is playing with someone else and Susie is not welcome to play with them.**
>
> **Following recess, Susie's teacher returns her paper with obvious disappointment regarding the quality of Susie's work. The teacher states, in a loud enough voice for the other students to hear her say that the work is unacceptable.**

Susie must take the paper home, re-work it, and have her parents sign it, thereby indicating that they were made aware of her sub-standard work.

Due to her vulnerable physical state, Susie perceives (Emotional Reality) that the teacher and other students see and think of her as "stupid, bad, dumb", and so forth. She is, therefore, imprinted with the thought and emotion, "I am stupid, bad, and dumb."

The Historical Reality is actually not what was said. Therefore, we see that Susie's condition of vulnerability created her *Emotional Truth* or *Reality* and not what others would report as to what actually happened (Historical Reality).

Now, if in fact the teacher had called her "stupid, bad, and dumb" and the other students heard her, then we are speaking of *Historical Reality.*

We can now see the indisputable interconnection of mind and body, at the exact interconnection of mind and body, at the exact moment of an event, which the mind-body has experienced through the individual perception of emotional traumatization. Here we must realize that at any given moment, an individual's emotional, mental, and/or physical state is in varying degrees of health.

To re-cap, the vulnerability of the mind-body system at any given time determines whether or not a Neuro Emotional Complex manifests. For indeed, the truths or reality of one's experience is

based on the *perceptions* of the individual and the condition of vulnerability at the time of any given event.

As cited earlier, the twins reported totally different memories or experiences from their childhood. This does not mean that one of them is lying or even hallucinating. Quite simply one twin, unlike her sister, was in a vulnerable state at the time of an event or experience that involved her father in some (perceived) negative way.

Dr. Walker states in the *Digest of Chiropractic Economics:*

> **"In the instant prior to, and at the moment of any potentially traumatizing event, an individual organism is apt to be in flux or in varying degrees of health, within any one of these dynamic subsystems."**

CLEARING THE NEURO EMOTIONAL COMPLEX

The Neuro Emotional Complex (NEC) is cleared by discovering/identifying the original event in which the patient experienced trauma (Historical or Emotional Reality). This is achieved through muscle testing either from a physical point of entry (such as a chronic or acute pain). In this case, Neuro Emotional Technique is utilized as opposed to NEAT. NET investigates through three categories: "Money, Love, or You." For example:

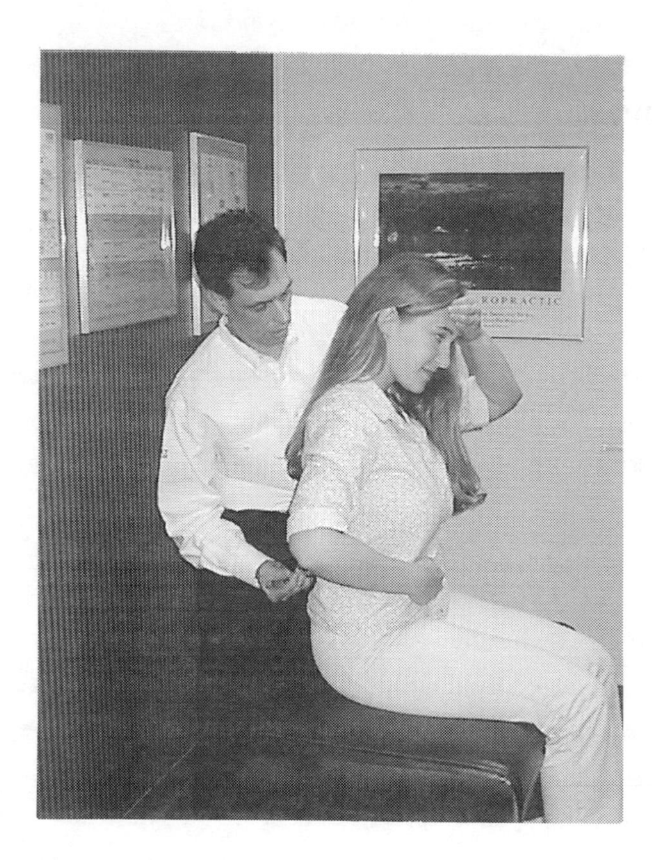

Clearing the Neuro Emotional Complex

1) Money - money, job, finance, career, etc.

2) Love - anyone you've ever loved, anyone who has ever loved you

3) You - you the person, man woman, friend, lover, spouse, teacher, parent, child, etc.

Neuro Emotional Anti-sabotage Technique investigates and detects through semantics. The patient makes statements (called Personal Declaratives) while the doctor muscle tests. A previously strong muscle now becomes weak thus indicating a Neuro Emotional Complex (NEC) is present.

Once the NEC is identified, the original traumatizing event is discovered, the NET doctor instructs the patient to

1) "make a picture" or Shapshot of the original event,

2) feel the emotion identified as the NEC,

3) place the other hand on the emotional points,

4) place another hand on the identified organ meridian point,

5) and the doctor adjusts the patient while directing deep breathing.

The correction by health care providers who are designated appropriate to "touch" the body is made by adjusting the corresponding vertebrae to the organ meridian access point. However, for the psychotherapist-psychologist, Dr. Walker has

TRADITIONAL PULSE POINTS

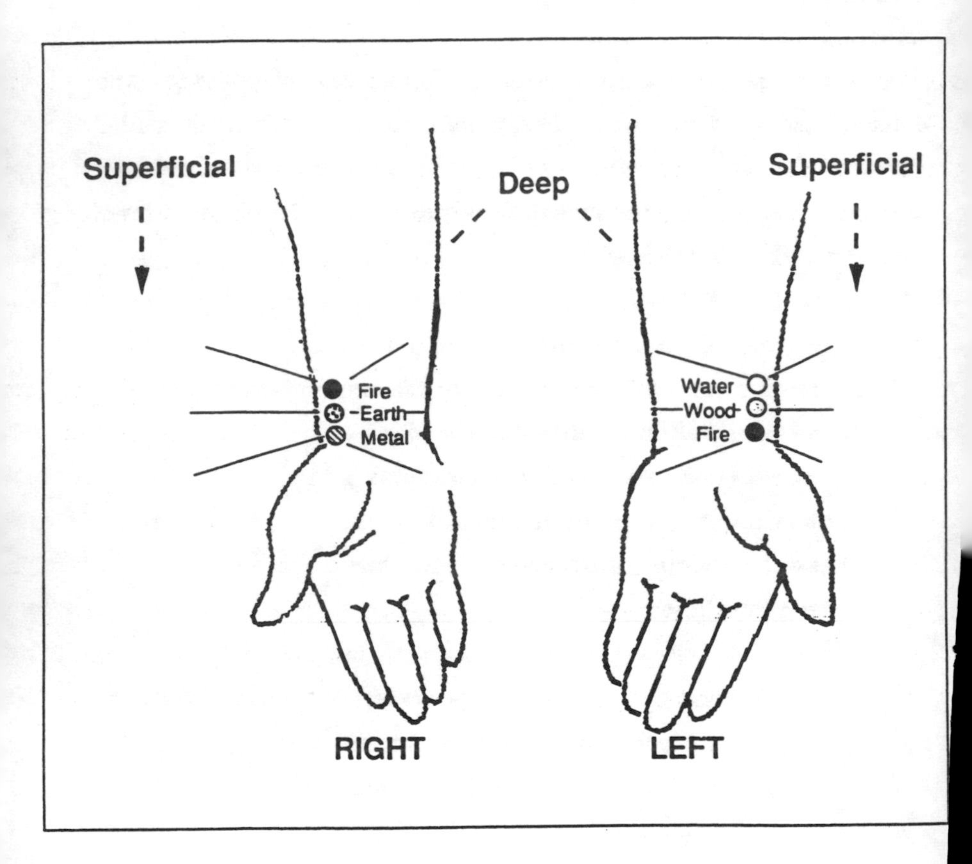

provided an alternative to the usual adjustive treatment. Utilizing the *Traditional Pulse Points* on the patient's wrists, following the discovery of the original event of traumatization, the patient can then be cleared of the Neuro Emotional Complex in a different mode and the SnapShot loses its charge.

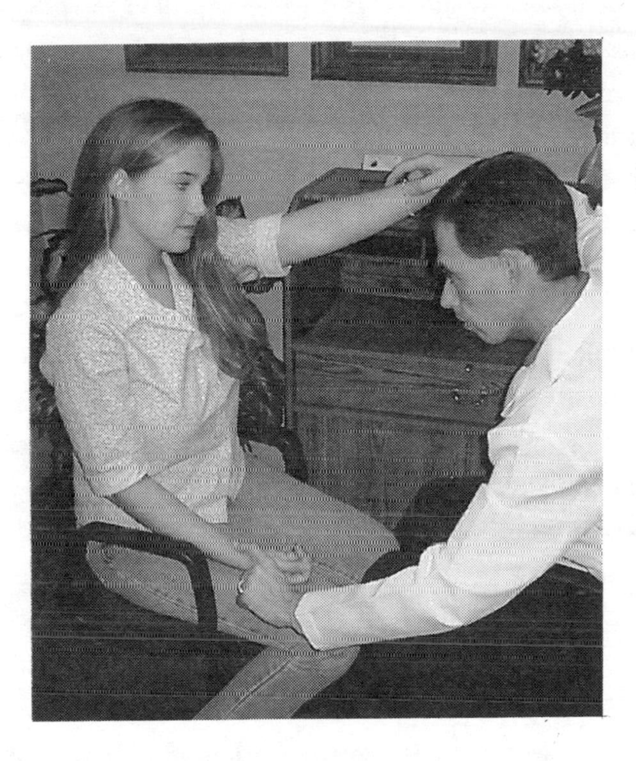

The Pulse Points

The patient is instructed to sit during this procedure because often the effect is so profound as to cause swaying and/or dizziness.

When the N.E.C. is cleared, the muscle, mis-aligned vertebrae, and meridians become stabilized. This is true even in the presence of the negative emotion. The negative emotion no longer "charges" the system and it loses its impact and vulnerability to re-stimulation.

Usually the patient feels better right away. They will experience instant relief, treatment effects are greatly extended, and re-aggravation is minimized.

At other times the relief is experienced later when the person's response or reaction pattern to the negative stimuli is altered. Often, the person will express feeling very relaxed, as though they could take a long nap.

Additionally, some people will often feel high energy pulsating through their system along with increased body temperature. Some even exhibit redness and flushing of the skin from the increased body heat. The entire treatment, from beginning to end, can be completed in a single office visit.

RE-TRACING

While symptoms can indicate a deteriorating condition, they can also indicate *improvement*. At times with NEAT/NET treatment, a phenomena will occur called *"Re-tracing."*

Re-tracing **is defined as the course of restoration from disease back to health. In other words, the case passes back through successive steps, in reverse order that it passed through in getting worse.**

When the physical body experiences symptoms of aches and pains due to an infection, the immune system kicks into gear and creates heat to fight the disharmony within the system. The added discomfort of fever is, in fact, eradicating the organisms responsible for the infection. The all too common response, however, is to alleviate the symptom via aspirin, and so forth. In fact, this actually can interfere with the natural healing process of the body. Hippocrates once said:

"Produce a fever, cure the disease."

Dr. Walker states that he has seen more re-tracing than in earlier years of his practice due to what he believes is the addition of nutrition supplementation, NET, and NET homeopathic remedies to structural techniques.

While it is observed that minor symptoms manifest, they subside quickly and fast improvement follows. Many times these re-tracing symptoms pass very quickly with no adverse symptoms at all. Dr. Walker suggests re-examination if the new symptoms continue for two or three days, especially severe or without any intermissions.

As of May, 1990, Dr. Walker reports that he had cleared some sixty thousand NECs and had never had to correct the same one twice. Hundreds of NET graduate doctors have duplicated this finding.

THE EMOTIONAL BODY

The emotional body is one in western civilization with which we attempt to ignore or dishonor. Example: There is a five letter word we tend to call young males who cry ... "sissy."

There is another condescending five letter word often utilized in describing females who express anger. You know this one ... it starts with the letter "B"!

It appears we have evolved as a culture ashamed of our emotions. How often, in a particularly moving scene at a movie theater do we cover our tears in shame or embarrassment lest others notice? How often do we tell our children, "Stop crying and be a BIG boy (or girl)?" This implies that the expression of emotion is bad, wrong, immature, or unacceptable.

This approach leads to repression of emotions which then leads to disease. An example of the American response to the emotional body, especially to the emotion of anger, as opposed to other cultures is shared in the following story about anger.

Years ago my husband and I sponsored a group of young people on a thirty-five day educational tour of Europe. We landed in Paris

in the morning, having flown overnight. We were so excited to be in Grand Paree!

We checked into our hotel and immediately departed with our tour guide. He was the perfectly envisioned stereotypical Parisian ... beret' hat, accent, effervescent personality, and all. Within minutes, he had us singing French songs. We had not even traveled two blocks from our hotel. We were having a grand time!

After about an hour, we traveled down a one-way cobblestone street. It was only wide enough for one lane of traffic and one row of parallel parked cars. Suddenly, we screeched to a halt. We looked up to see a woman attempting to parallel park her small car. She was having great difficulty in doing so.

Our tour guide sat patiently for her first two attempts. On the third failure, he turned off the engine, got out, and walked over to the damsel in distress. We assumed our wonderful guide was going to politely assist her.

In a few moments, however, we Americans were riveted to what we considered to be a shocking scene! The two of them stood in the street screaming in French at one another. While flailing their arms in the air, they never once touched, nor struck one another. Nevertheless, we sat in shocked discomforted silence, glancing away only long enough to see if someone would stop them or call the police!

However, as suddenly as they had started this interchange, they stopped. The woman re-entered her car, our guide returned to the

bus. We watched gratefully as she successfully parked her car. Our guide drove down the street and by the time we had reached the next intersection he was *singing* again!

Throughout the remainder of our day-long tour, we Americans never quite recovered from this event. We sat in silence and remained unresponsive to his jollity. We were convinced that we had a "madman" for a tour guide.

In retrospect, I am certain when he returned home that evening he did not enter his home slamming the door, yelling to his wife, "Do you know what this crazy woman did today?" I am also quite sure that he had forgotten it before he turned the next corner. In contrast, I, as an American, am still talking about it some thirty years later!

It is unhealthy for human beings to fear the emotional body, especially the expression of any emotion which we might term negative. There are constructive ways in which to express the emotions of which we fear.

PRIMAL PAIN

In 1970, Dr. Janov was baffled by a patient who upon his crying out "Mommy! Daddy!" (at Janov's request), was suddenly writhing on the floor. He was screeching loudly and eventually went into small convulsions. The patient then released a "piercing, deathlike scream

that rattled the walls." Afterward, all the man could say was: "I made it! I don't know what happened, but I can FEEL!"

That was the impetus for Dr. Janov to develop Primal Therapy, based on the theory that "primal pains" are early hurts upon which all later neuroses is built. These pains often are not consciously felt because they are diffused throughout the entire system where they affect body organs, muscles, the blood and lymph system. Finally then, they distort the way we behave. This is reported from Janov's book *Primal Scream.*

EMPTINESS, REPRESSION AND THE ANGRY SOCIETY

In 1953, Rollo May wrote of the "hollow people" in his book *Man's Search For Himself.* He believed that the chief problem with people was emptiness. He stated:

> ***"...the chief problem of the middle decade of***
> ***the twentieth century is EMPTINESS..not only***
> ***that many people do not know what they want,***
> ***they often do not have any clear idea of what***
> ***they FEEL. It soon becomes evident that their***
> ***underlying problem is that they have no definite***
> ***experience of their own desires or wants. Thus***
> ***they feel swayed this way and that, with painful feelings***

of powerlessness, because they feel vacuous, EMPTY."

These are difficulties present in all decades. Some fifty years later we continue to struggle with the emotional body. In addition to the general malaise of emptiness, now in the nineties going into the new millennium, we are seeing the results of years of emotional repression erupting (as in the kettle boiling over!). This is "tell-tale," revealing our *angry society.*

Dr. George A. Wilson, in his article, *a Brief Background On The Traditional Psychological Model, The NEC and The Snapshot Of The Neuro Emotional Technique (N.E.T.), states:*

> ***"...too many of us inwardly are a seething mass of emotional resentments, created by emotional sore spots, needing only something to brush us the wrong way in order to cause an emotional flare up."***

This is evidenced by the rise in violence and crime. There is often non-directive or random crime such as drive-by shootings, or the famous Luby's Cafeteria murders, the random shooting spree at McDonalds, and perhaps most tragically tell-tell of all...the killings of our children by other children.

The all-time high drug abuse with its concomitant crime is yet another symptom of a society seeking an anesthetic for the deep inner psychic pain of the emotional and spiritual bodies!

The bombing of the Murrah Federal building in Oklahoma City is another most shocking example of societal-repressed anger. The entire world watched in horror, stunned and in disbelief that such a cold blooded event could occur in the Heartland of America! *Truly, these events must be a "wake-up" call!*

An estimated 200,000 to 400,000 young people per year are locked up in private psychiatric hospitals. Well over one and a half million children are being prescribed drugs to control their behavior either at home and/or at school. The number of children prescribed Ritalin in the United States compared to the rest of the world is to compare the size of New York's World Trade Center (American children) to a two thousand square foot house (the remaining children of the entire world)!

Throughout the history and evolution of humankind, however, we have been provided the development and provision of that which has appeared to be timely for the existing period...its ills, challenges and progress.

As we enter the year 2000, we can appreciate the fact that more discoveries, development and changes have occurred in this century than any other in the history of the world.

I, along with multitudes of others, believe *Neuro Emotional Anti-sabotage Technique* (NEAT) to be a major breakthrough at such a time when the need for rapid change, treatment and balance are tantamount for humankind.

EMOTIONS AND THE ORGAN MERIDIAN ACCESS POINTS

The spoken word is a powerful thing. Our euphemisms within language patterns have long been of great interest to me. While I am not nor do I claim to be, a linguist, I firmly believe that most, if not all of our euphemistic expressions are unconscious wisdom expressing itself. Some examples are:

"He makes me sick to my stomach!" (Disgust)
"She galls me to the core!" (Galled, Anger)
"My heart is broken." (Abandoned, Deserted)

Dr. Scott Walker, as well as many others, such as Louise Hay, R.N., who authored *You Can Heal Your Life*, have believed and postulated that the human organism will hold certain emotions in certain organ meridian points or parts of the body.

The following chart is a run-down of the emotions that Dr. Walker believes to be stored in various organ meridian access points.

The emotions do not cross the solid lines. However, emotions can be held in the organ meridians where there are broken lines, i.e. Gall Bladder and Liver could hold the same NECs, Stomach, Spleen, and Pancreas can hold the same NECs, and so forth.

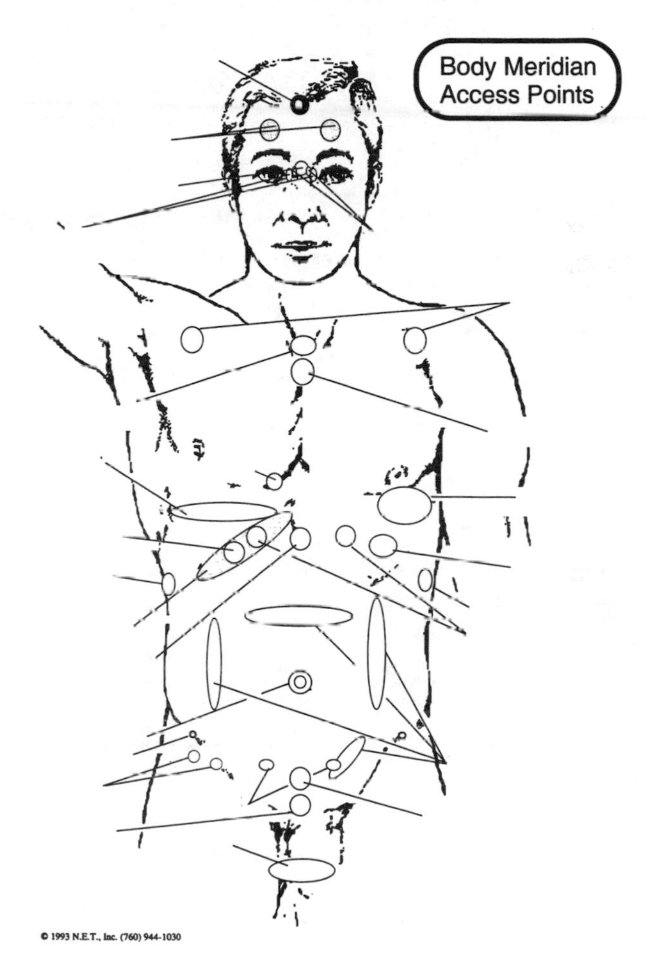

Simplified N E T© Master Chart

Organ	Emotion	Associated States	Remedy
Stomach	Over sympathetic	Disgust, expanded importance of self, obsession, egotistic, despair, nervous, stifled	*EARTH* Remedy
Spleen Pancreas	Low self-esteem	Lives through others, over concern, hopelessness, lack of control over events, worried, distrust	
Large Intestine	Dogmatically positioned	Crying, compelled to neatness, defensive	*METAL* Remedy
Lung	Grief	Sadness, yearning, cloudy thinking, anguish	
Bladder	Paralyzed will	Miffed, timid, inefficient, wishy-washy, comme çi-comme ça	*WATER* Remedy
Kidney	Fear	Dread, bad memory, contemplated	
Gall Bladder	Resentment	Galled, stubborn, emotionally repressed, depressed, indecisive	*WOOD* Remedy
Liver	Anger	Irrationality, frustration, aggression	
Small Intestine	Lost, Vulnerable	Abandoned, deserted, absent mindedness, insecurity, profoundly deep unrequited love	*FIRE* Remedy
Heart	Frightfully overjoyed	Abnormal (inappropriate) laughing, lack of emotion, rapid mannerisms and speech, talkative	
Thyroid Adrenals	Muddled instability	Muddled thinking, emotional instability, up and down, can't figure it out	*FIRE* Remedy
Prostate Testicles Ovaries Uterus Pituitary	Non-thinking, Non-emotive	Depleted, suppressed, sluggish memory, vivid dreaming	*FIRE* Remedy

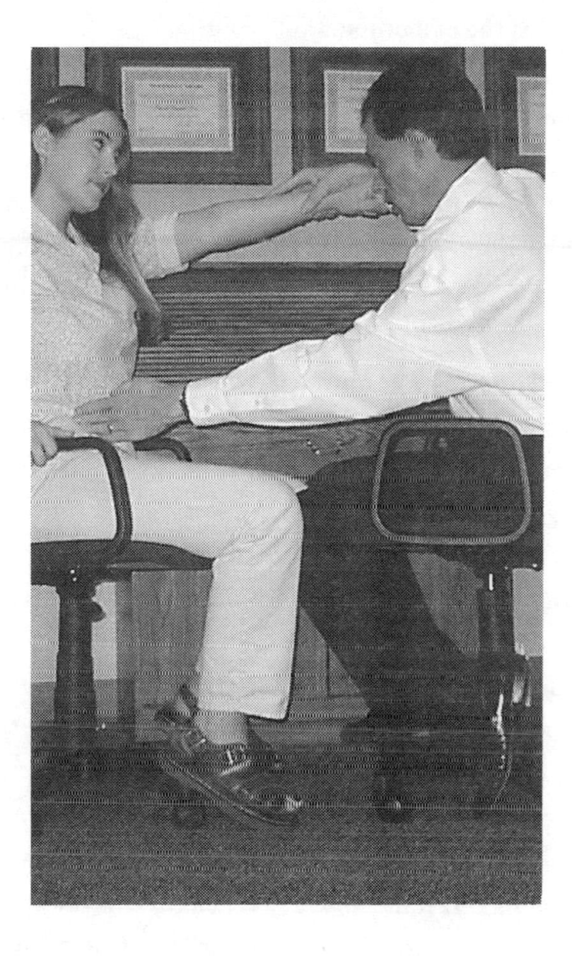

Locating the Organ Meridian Access Point of the NEC

Dr. Clyde Porter in his 1989 book, *Where Healing Waters Meet*, clearly explains the embodiment of trauma:

"It is not only early life experiences which are stored somatically; almost all illness or injury has a somatic component regardless of when in life they occur. An automobile accident is a good example of this. Painful neck spasm is a common occurrence after a whiplash injury. One reason the neck muscles go into spasm is preventive. They tighten up to avert further injury. The problem here is that long after the accident is over, the muscle spasm remains. In a sense, the spasm is a somatic memory of the accident. But more than just a muscle tightness is stored as a result of the trauma. Many emotions surface in those few moments before the impact of an accident, especially if a person is fore-warned and waiting for this inevitable trauma to occur. All feelings present at the time of the accident are then stored in the body along with the physical trauma. In this case, healing requires not just releasing the physical pain, but releasing emotional pain within the body as well. Somatic tissue functions as a secondary storage facility for the brain. An automobile accident shows us how this takes place. The sound of screeching tires, the sight of an upcoming tree, the touch of an out of control steering wheel, are the sensory cues which cause us to hold our bodies tight and to experience fear in the few moments before impact. After impact

the continuing spasms and fear are, in effect, stored images of these critical cues. Here, muscle spasm is a form of somatic memory arising from three different sources...seeing, hearing, and touching."

Experts generally agree that 80 to 95 per cent of our actions are controlled by our unconscious. Thus, it is reasonable to conclude that habits rule the daily life of us all. When *WE* are in charge or in control of our lives, we develop healthy, positive habits. The result, of course, is *FREEDOM.* The more self directed we are, the more freedom we have. A. J. Golombos, astrophysicist, once defined "freedom" as:

"FREEDOM IS HAVING CONTROL OVER YOUR OWN PROPERTY."

"Property" is here defined as "our attention or focus and our behavior patterns." We have the ability to create "failure" habits or "success" habits!

Neuro Emotional Complexes create "failure" habits because they are in control! One can create, verbalize, and write positive affirmations "ad infinitum" without the successful outcome sought. This is because the NEC is in charge or in control. The NEC is therefore sabotaging your positive dreams and desires!

When NECs are imprinted, a lack of choice is experienced and goals are unfulfilled. Poor health, and painful emotions may result. Dr. Walker emphasizes that the "NECs are not judged harshly by the wise doctor."

When NECs are removed, our organism's natural, resourceful selves are allowed to work properly. The natural goal-seeking mechanism can return to optimal function as it was intended! The balance or homeostasis is as natural and powerful as Mother Earth rotating on her axis.

If we are not in control of our lives and habits, Neuro Emotional Complexes (NECs) are controlling us. This occurs in much the same way that the puppeteer controls the puppet.

FAILURE and/or SUCCESS CAN BECOME HABIT.

* * * * * * * * * *

"WHAT N.E.A.T. IS AND WHAT IT IS NOT"

Dr. Walker has written a treatise that should clarify further as he states some values and boundaries of Neuro Emotional Anti-sabotage Technique. It is as follows:

"N.E.A.T. is a methodology of finding and removing neurological aberrations (Neuro Emotional Complexes) in the human

organism. These aberrations have, as a component part, specific emotional neurophysiological patterns. It is ultimately a method of finding and removing vertebral subluxations. Emotions are traditionally thought of as being normal functions of human beings which normally pose no neurophysiological problem. Occasionally, emotional trauma in the presence of a neurological deficit causes a neurological pattern (NEC) in the body which does not resolve of itself. N.E.A.T. seeks to normalize this pattern by a physiological change, results of a structural intervention from the spine. Any psychological aspects of this trauma should be referred out to the appropriate health care professional, such as a psychologist or psychiatrist. N.E.A.T. is not psychology or psychiatry. It does not involve any type of psychotherapy or a 'talk it out' approach to emotions. Additionally, N.E.A.T. does not deal with the spiritual realm. It does not exorcise demons or entities. It does not predict the future or deal in any way with parapsychology. It does not make claims as to what may have happened in the past. It does not tell people what their plan of action may, must, or should be for the future."

Dr. Scott Walker

DIAGNOSING

In both the Neuro Emotional Anti-sabotage Technique and Neuro Emotional Technique processes, the subject of diagnosing is most important. Dr. Walker discusses the various modes of diagnosing from the "Inside Out" diagnosis, the "Outside In" diagnosis, to the far out "Outside In" diagnosis.

An "*INSIDE*" diagnosis, for example, can be accomplished by:

X-ray
MRI
Mammograms
Blood/urine analysis

An *"OUTSIDE IN"* diagnosing could be accomplished by calibrating or observing:

A patient's skin color
Sclera or streaking of the eyes
Facial expressions
Posture
Gait
Gestures
Physical coordination at work
Mental efficiency at work

NET doctors diagnose from even further out by standing way, way back. They diagnose by:

How their patients relate to others

How their patients relate to the universe

What their patient's attitudes are in the world

What the contents of the patient's offices and homes are displaying, as in signs, slogans, sayings

Their patient's lack of success, as in divorce, unemployment

Their patient's frequent illnesses

Their patient's so-called 'accidents'

Their patient's lack of prosperity

Dr. Khelly Webb says:

"For one to come the closest to understanding how N.E.T. and N.E.A.T. works, one must just experience it. Then it becomes easier to understand."

Dr. Scott Walker visualizes seven elements or contributing factors in the description and make-up surrounding N.E.A.T.. In the next Addendum, these seven elements and contributing factors will briefly be presented, indicating how they are relevant to N.E.T. and N.E.A.T..

ADDENDUM III

"Psyche and body react sympathetically to each other. A change in the psyche produces a change in the structure of the body and conversely, a change in the structure of the body produces a change in the psyche."

Aristotle

THE SEVEN ELEMENTS IN NET AND NEAT

1. **Psychology'S Subconscious Principle**
2. **Pavlovian Reflexes (Stimulus Response)**
3. **Korsybski's General Semantics**
4. **Parker's Principles**
5. **Chiropractic Spinal Adjusting and Muscle Testing**
6. **Acupuncture's Five Element Law**
7. **Homeopathic Energization Principles**

(These are not listed in order of priority or importance.)

PSYCHOLOGY'S SUBCONSCIOUS PRINCIPLE

The traditional psychological model embodies the concept of *older events influencing more recent events of the present.*

Virginia Satir, world renowned for her development of Family Therapy once said that if she was shown a coping difficulty in a person's present life experience, then she could trace it (coping difficulty) back to an unresolved early life (negative) experience.

When our primary instinct of survival is threatened, we undergo an emotional or psychological response. This response is then coded into the system and replayed whenever a similar environmental situation (stimulus) arises. Neuro Linguistic Programming (NLP) terms these codings as "anchors."

The subconscious mind sets up a reflex reaction to this primary incident as it, or a similar incident, is replayed in the present. The traumatic originating event can lead the body to become imbalanced or dis-harmonized. This may be expressed as a dysfunction. If the dysfunction is toxic enough, it eventually creates disease.

Sigmund Freud, (1856-1939) was an Austrian physician who was considered to be the founder of psychoanalysis. He created an entirely new approach to understanding the human personality by his demonstration of the existence and force of the unconscious.

In essence, he founded a new medical discipline. He formulated basic therapeutic procedures which, in modified form are applied widely to the present-day treatment of neuroses and psychoses.

Freud was heralded for his collaborative work on hysteria with Viennese physician Josef Breuer (1842-1925). They presented their

preliminary paper in 1893. Two years later, in an expanded form, entitled *"Studies on Hysteria"*, they published their findings.

In this work, symptoms of hysteria were ascribed to manifestations of undischarged emotional energy which was associated with forgotten psychic traumas. The therapeutic procedure involved the use of hypnosis, whereby the patient was led to recall and re-enact the traumatic experience. A discharged and catharsis of emotions causing the symptoms ensued.

Freud later abandoned the use of hypnosis as a cathartic procedure. He substituted the investigation of the patient's spontaneous flow of thoughts, called "free association," to reveal unconscious mental processes as the root of the neurotic disturbance. In his clinical observations, he found evidence of the mental mechanisms of "repression" and "resistance."

"Repression" was described as a device which operated unconsciously and made the memory of painful or threatening events inaccessible to the conscious mind. "Resistance" was defined as the unconscious defense against awareness of these repressed experiences in order to avoid the resultant anxiety. He traced the course of unconscious processes by using the patient's free associations (language) to guide his interpretation of both dreams and slips of speech.

To counter this primary emotional trauma, many psychotherapeutic techniques have been developed and utilized.

Psychiatrist, Elizabeth Kubler-Ross, M.D., names one of her techniques "mattress work." This is a therapeutic process in which one relives an original primary trauma and releases emotion through a physical pounding on a mattress or other safe surface. Today, many excellent psychiatric hospitals include an "anger room" in which patients can express and physically release trauma by pounding the padded walls and floors.

Janov's Primal Scream Therapy, mentioned earlier, is another method of physically releasing emotions. Deep massage therapy work will also evoke old emotional traumas and then facilitate the release of the emotion.

Virginia Satir developed the "Family Reconstruction" psychodrama method whereby a "parts party" is utilized. During the *parts party*, other individuals actually play out the original family member's parts. This allows the trauma to be replayed, released, resolved, and re-written.

Neuro Linguistic Programming primarily utilizes the visual, auditory, and kinesthetic senses to de-sensitize or extinguish the primary psycho-trauma. It is then re-programmed with a positive, constructive, and resourceful program.

Ericksonian Hypnosis, developed from the work of Franz Mesmer in the eighteenth century, is another method utilized in NLP, along with various other therapies.

All of these psychological models embody the concept that older events influence present events and reinforce the existence of the *Body-Mind* connection.

PAVLOVIAN REFLEXES

In 1909, Yerkes and Morgulis published a study conducted by Ivan Pavlov. In this experiment, Pavlov gave his dog a piece of meat. The dog's normal response of salivation was observed. This same procedure was repeated while a bell was rung (at the same time the meat was introduced).

After repeated trials, it was observed that the dog salivated solely in response to the sound of the bell. Since dogs do not ordinarily respond with salivation to the sound of a bell alone, this was a learned association response to an experience, (in this case, meat to the bell). This principle became known as the "*conditioned response.*"

After observing the conditioning process of his dog's salivation (physiological response) to the stimulus of both the bell and the meat, Pavlov discovered that this response continued for a period of time.

After many trials *without* the stimulus of the bell, Pavlov noted that the conditioned response (salivation) would extinguish. This process came to be known as "*extinction.*"

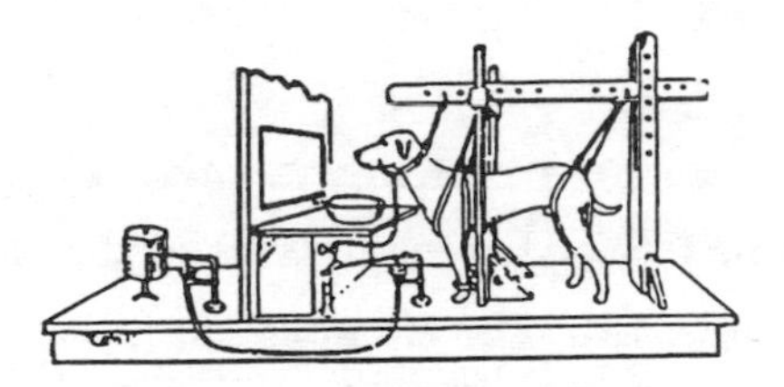

Pavlov's Dog -From Yerkes and Morgulis (1909).

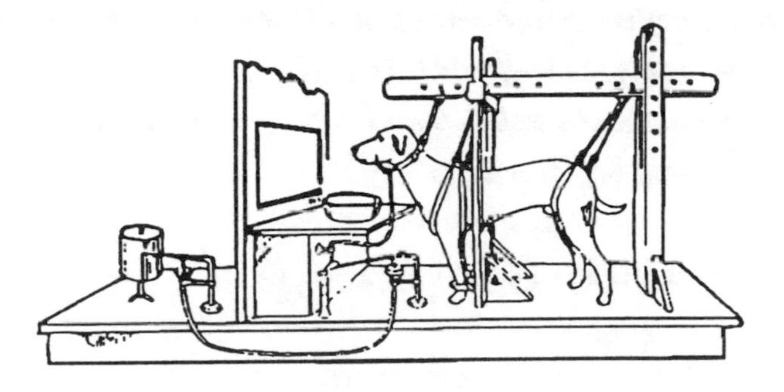

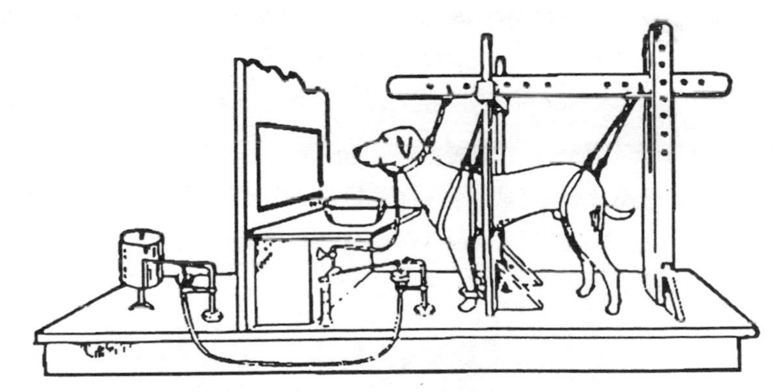

The extinction phenomenon occurs frequently in various modes of learning. Calculus, algebra, or foreign language skills tend to fade when these acquired skills are not used. The old adage applies, "use it or lose it." Other learned skills such as skiing, or riding a bicycle never seem to extinguish. Why is this? Dr. Walker has said:

> ***"In survival-driven states, extinction is a normal psychological process, but at times may not occur in the human with prior physiological deficits at the time of emotionally-impacted conditioning. This allows for N.E.C. (Neuro Emotional Complex) formation (which contains within it a conditioned response resistant to extinction.)"***

He further purports that a Neuro Emotional Complex contains:

**** a conditioned response (a learned response, by association, to a specific experience)***
**** a specific emotion (anger, low self-esteem, abandoned, resentment, grief, and so forth***
**** a meridian imbalance (a weak meridian point, detected by muscle testing***
**** a specific active organ reflex point (weak organ reflex)***
**** a resistance to extinction (other methods or adjustments failed to extinguish)***

***** a vulnerability to re-stimulation and repression causing re-enforcement (magnetic process of the Emotional Complex to "like experiences) and**

***** a "charged and often re-callable memory picture" or "snapshot."**

Dr. Scott Walker

Now, again we see the indisputable interconnection of mind and body. At the exact moment when an event which the mind-body has experienced through the individual perception of emotional traumatization, the Pavlovian Conditioned Response Reflex was activated.

To repeat, an emotionally traumatic event in one's life may or may not create, record or imprint a Neuro Emotional Complex. It is important to remember that the *state* of the system (physical, mental, emotional) at the time of the traumatic event determines whether or not a Neuro Emotional Complex is formed. The NEC, with its property of being resistant to extinction or not, is imprinted when the system is in a state of *vulnerability*.

The following is an analogy for the purpose of clarification:

On the drive to the office for a very important business meeting, someone rear-ends you, totaling your car. You are left with a whiplash and head injury. The condition of your system is ripe

for the formation of a Neuro Emotional Complex. The *physical* body is in jeopardy due to the accident trauma to the neck. The *emotional* body is vulnerable due to your anger with the other driver because you felt that he was not alert. The *mental* body missed a very important transmission of information at a busines meeting due to the accident.

Everyone's system is different and unique. What might create an NEC in one individual, will not do so in another. Our truths as individuals are just that, *highly individual.* Our "truths" are formulated by our perceptions (how we interpret, comprehend, and discern our environment through physical sensations). These truths are based on many factors regarding the condition of the system at the time of any particular experienced event.

Rossi and Cheek, mentioned earlier, pose this thought:

> ***"...most Pavlovian and Skinnerian conditioning actually involves an important element of state dependent memory, learning, and behavior (SDMLB) that frequently is not recognized by researchers."***

They further state:

> ***"A psychological model (Rossi, 1986) of memory and learning that includes the state dependent nature of physiological homeostasis as well as of memory and learning will be required***

for a more complete understanding of the clinical phenomena of depth psychology and psychosomatic medicine."

If emotional trauma occurs at a time of physical, emotional, and mental strength, the system will, generally, return to homeostasis (a relatively stable state of equilibrium or balance).

Dr. Walker summarizes by stating:

"...it is important to emphasize that not all emotions are incorporated in Neuro Emotional Complexes, but all N.E.C.s incorporate emotions. N.E.C.s are the aberrant interface between the lowered resistance of the body, (including structural and biochemical factors), the memory, and the emotions."

THE IMPORTANCE OF LANGUAGE

The study of meaning in language and the response of the human organism to that meaning is important to discuss. Neuro Linguistic Programming, developed from the language patterns of Virginia Satir and Milton Erickson, has recognized the power of language and its symbolism for each representational system via the following:

1) visual - sense of sight
2) auditory - sense of hearing
3) kinesthetic - sense of feelings; perception of muscular

movement, tension, skin, joints, tendons, derived from the functioning of afferent nerves connected with same.

Through these senses, people experience or perceive within individual contexts, as individual people.

Neuro Emotional Anti-sabotage Technique (NEAT) utilizes the observances of verbalization of words or phrases. These are called Personal Declarative Statements (PDS) which may cause the muscle or body to go weak. The muscle going weak indicates there is a *charge* on the words or phrases and a Neuro Emotional Complex (NEC) is indicated. During the process of search, playing detective, and discovery, the NEC is discharged (cleared) and the associated conditioned response is thereby therapized.

It is important to now briefly discuss Korzybski's semantics as a contributing factor in understanding the Neuro Emotional Anti-sabotage Technique.

KORSYBSKI'S GENERAL SEMANTICS

Alfred Korzybski was among the first to formulate neuro linguistic and neuro-semantic disciplines, referred to as "semantics." He originally formulated this system of discipline for the understanding and correction of human mis-evaluating. General semantics can be referred to as a system, (i.e., a set of related propositions or statements).

Korzybski's major cumulative work was concerned with what he called structure, (a complex of relationships and order). The structures with which he most concerned himself may be laid out as follows:

Structure 1) the non-verbal world as in physics, neuro-biology, moving cumulatively, in a time-binding manner, to the ongoing present
Structure 2) the human organism, as a whole, in an environment at a given date, particularly focused on its highly evolved nervous system and brain
Structure 3) human behavior, what people do and say, as an expression of all of the above

Korzybski claimed that if we study and apply general semantics, we can better assess, evaluate, and become more self and world-aware. Having done so, we can make new formulations for ourselves to improve our lot, both personally and globally.

PARKER'S PRINCIPLES

James W. Parker, D.C., founder of the Parker College of Chiropractic in Dallas, Texas expounded upon and popularized the notion of "Quality Nerve Interference." He accomplished this before

there was ever any scientific proof of an underlying physiological basis (for it). He developed a set of principles called "*Parker's Principles for SHH.*" The SHH is an abbreviation for Success, Health, and Happiness. They are as follows:

1. **UP - Understood Principles plus Unified Procedure equal Unlimited Patients.**
2. **SHH - My Success, Health and Happiness are determined by what I think, the way I act, and how I feel.**
3. **My Inner Success is not a matter of adding anything, an acquisition; it is purely a ridding, a shedding process.**
4. **I will be free of negative emotions as soon as I stop justifying and defending them.**
5. **What I see in the Universe sees me.**
6. **My level of inner success is determined by the amount of truth I can take without getting angry or upset.**
7. **It is impossible for me to begin to learn what I think I already know, or to accept a solution to a problem I don't feel I have.**
8. **Negative feelings toward others punish me on the spot, for I am a chained slave to anyone I dislike.**
9. **There is no philosophy by which I can do a thing if I think I cannot.**

10. From this moment on:

   a. **I will not be immersed in negativity because I will always embrace positiveness in some way.**

   b. **I will not be baptized in pessimism because I will be bathed in optimism.**

   c. **I will not prattle in my conversation about problems because I will meditate on solutions.**

   d. **I will not be consumed with what is wrong in the world because I will be saturated with the good in the world.**

11. I know that 99% of failure is self-inflicted, "If it is to be, it is up to me."

12. I will anticipate the good even during the bad.

13. I will reflect with joy on all past events and I will see the blessings in them.

As so indicated by these very eloquent and wise principles as contributing factors, NEAT and NET are very positive processes.

CHIROPRACTIC SPINAL ADJUSTING AND MUSCLE TESTING

Chiropractic Spinal Adjusting was discovered by D.D. Palmer in 1895 when he adjusted the vertebra of a deaf janitor and found that his hearing was immediately restored. Palmer reasoned that the nervous system controlled all bodily activity and that mis-aligned vertebrae interfered with good nervous system function. He subsequently went on to establish the chiropractic profession, as we know it today.

Muscle testing is one avenue by which we can *access* the human system's computer. It plays an integral part in both detecting and diagnosing the location of a physiologically held or stored Neuro Emotional Complex (NEC). It "smokes out" the "snapshot" (visualization of a specific memory or event) and the NEC, in combination with the semantics or language patterns.

In 1964, George J. Goodheart, Jr., D.C. made some profound therapeutic discoveries and observations concerning the function of muscles. He found, for example, that the physiological strength of a muscle could be rapidly altered by merely touching an associated reflex point. An apparently healthy and strong muscle, during manual muscle testing, would weaken under certain stimuli.

His discoveries since that time have already become legendary with his introduction of Applied Kinesiology (AK). The major

A Doctor Muscle Testing A Patient

premise of AK is that the response of the neuromuscular system to emotional, physical, and chemical stimuli can operate as an indicator of the functional status of the patient's physiology. Dr. Kris Peterson, in his research paper, *"Phobic Muscle Testing"* states:

> ***"AK holds that the interpretation of the patient's response to this clinical testing procedure can compliment clinical testing diagnostic procedures, thereby aiding the healthcare provider in the therapeutic decision-making process."***

Manual muscle testing relates the ability of a muscle to "lock" in response to a particular stimulus, (chemical, physical, or emotional).

A "lock" response is a strong muscle response. It is not related to the actual strength of the muscle being tested, but to the sense that there is a specific firmness or resistance to the examiner's pressure.

A "weak" muscle response to any stimulus could indicate a functional maladaptive physiological response. If a patient's thought of a particular memory or emotion produces a weakness of the tested muscle, the patient is then considered to be physiologically incongruent with that memory or thought concept. This is precisely where and how we discover Neuro Emotional Complexes (NECs). In a recent study, assessing the reliability of the muscle test in distinguishing emotional congruency with semantic stimuli was highly

significant. This research project was headed by Dan Monti, M.D., a psychiatrist on faculty at the Jefferson Medical College in Philadelphia, PA. He was assisted in this study by Drs. John Sinnott, D.C. and Marc Marchese, PhD. Dr. Monti is also the chairman of the O.N.E. Foundation's Research Committee.

In this study, participants made true and false statements. The results showed that the body exhibited a consistent response when congruent with the statement. The body exhibited a different, yet consistent, response to a non-congruent statement.

The responses were measured using pressure-sensitive muscle testing equipment. In so doing, Dr. Monti hoped to validate the muscle test as a functional neuromuscular tool for assessing emotional congruency. The next phase of his study will evaluate EMG responses in the muscle test and correlate congruency with standard biofeedback measurements.

We anxiously await the results of his continuing research. As practitioners, we have high expectations as the efficacy of our clinical results will be greatly enhanced.

ACUPUNCTURE'S FIVE ELEMENT LAW

Through the centuries, the Chinese healing art of acupuncture has been utilized to relieve pain and suffering for millions of

individuals throughout the world Acupuncture has also helped thousands of individuals quit smoking, release weight, and so forth.

The World Health Organization (WHO) has reported that at least forty-seven different kinds of diseases are treatable by this art. In China, however, there are more than two hundred types of diseases which are treated with acupuncture.

In a tentative bow to centuries of Chinese medical research, the Food and Drug Administration (FDA) has decreed that acupuncture needles are as respectable a medical tool as either a syringe or scalpel. They will continue their study of this ancient healing art.

The Chinese live in the elements. They trust the order and flow of Universal Law and the changes therein. As they recognize the changes of the world around them, they also recognize the world within. They recognize these inner patterns go through the same cycles of the seasons within themselves.

The Elements are recreated within as well as in the world. New life in the spring corresponds to "new life" within self. Blooming that takes place in summer is also represented by the blooming and flourishing within self. We, as living beings, are also the Elements. Diane Connelly, PhD speaks of this in *Traditional Acupuncture: The Law of the Five Elements:*

> ***"Nature is without and within us, each of us every moment. We are a replica of the universe passing from season to season in a***

natural unending cycle of life. The interaction of the Five Elements brings harmony and everything is in order. The concept of health follows laws inherent in Life Energy, inherent in Nature."

Energy, as spoken of here, is the force we call life. The Chinese term this energy "*chi.*" The Japanese call it "*ki.*" We can liken this energy to the rivers, lakes, seas and oceans of the Earth. This vital life force flows within us in pathways in like manner.

The Chinese consider good health to be a state of energy balance within the human body. Body tissues and structures are primarily viewed in relation to the energy which activates them. Furthermore, this energy will manifest in the polar forms of what is called "Yin" and "Yang" energy.

One could think of "yin" and "yang" as the negative and positive poles, respectively, within a flow. Of "yin" and "yang" each is separate and distinct in expression, yet both are a part of the current. There is no absolute yin or yang. Each contains a portion of the other.

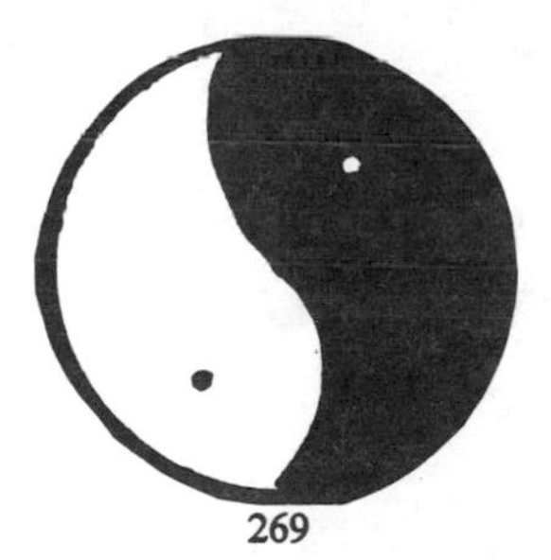

Thousands of years ago the Chinese established the five basic elements that interact, in a creative cycle, to form all other substances. These elements are 1) Fire, 2) Water, 3) Earth, 4) Metal, and 5) Wood.

Each of these five elements is associated with a body organ. Each is assigned at least one yin and one yang organ. The yin organs include the liver, lungs, spleen, pancreas, kidneys, heart, and heart constrictor.

The yang organs include the large intestine, small intestine, stomach, bladder, gall bladder, and triple heater (the sister function of Circulation Sex). They are identified with the five elements in the following mode:

Fire: yin - heart, heart constrictor
yang - small intestine, triple heater
Earth: yin - spleen, pancreas
yang - stomach
Metal: yin - lungs
yang - large intestine
Water: yin - kidneys
yang - bladder
Wood: yin - liver
yang - gall bladder

The Five Elements have a relationship in which each submits to the element preceding it, in the following order: wood, fire, earth,

metal, and water. These relationships are called the *Relationships of Mutual Generation.* For example:

- **Wood engenders fire,**
- **Fire engenders earth,**
- **Earth engenders metal,**
- **Metal engenders water,**
- **Water engenders wood.**

These relationships are also referred to as *Relationship of Mother-Child.* Wood is the Mother of fire, fire the Mother of earth, and so forth. This Mother-Child Relationship is also called the *Relationship of Mutual Harmony.*

The Elements* have the tendency to subdue the second following Element in the chain. This is called the *Relationship of Mutual Subjugation* (conquest). In other words, wood overcomes earth, earth overcomes water, water overcomes fire, and so forth. This is called the *Relationship of Mutual Fear.

The Relationship of Overcoming and Engendering is called the *Relationship of Reflected Conquest* (overcoming the conqueror). This relationship indicates phenomena which are mutually-related, as in the following:

The Relationship of Mutual Generation:

Wood generates Fire...fire is generated, using wood as fuel,

Fire generates Earth...burned out fire becomes ashes and ultimately earth.

Earth generates Metal...metal is generated inside the earth.

Metal engenders Water...water is often found in land with much metal.

Water engenders Wood...wood is from trees which absorb water from soil.

The Relationship of Subjugation can be explained as:

Wood overcomes Earth...wood, as a tree absorbs nourishment from the earth.

Earth overcomes Water...water can be damned by earth or be absorbed into it.

Water overcomes Fire...water extinguishes fire.

Fire overcomes Wood...metal tools can cut wood.

These five elements are generated and destroyed according to a law of cyclical interaction. By substituting a corresponding yin organ for each element we see that the heart (fire) aids or reinforces the action of the spleen-pancreas (earth); the spleen-pancreas reinforces the lungs (metal); the lungs reinforce the kidneys (water); and so forth.

Conversely, fire melts metal, metal cuts wood, and water extinguishes fire. On the other hand, water is without effect on earth, earth does not affect wood, wood does not affect metal, metal does not affect fire, and fire does not affect water.

Following this chain we then see that the kidneys do not affect the spleen-pancreas, the spleen-pancreas does not affect the liver, the liver does not affect the lungs, the lungs do not affect the heart, and the heart does not affect the kidneys.

"Even the tiny ladybug
shares the responsibility for the
intricate balance of the universe
~~~helping to keep it
beautiful and productive...."

Author unknown

The energy giving life to the body circulates through well-defined channels, called *meridians*. These meridians are like imaginary lines joining a series of points. Ten of the meridians are associated with structural organs. These organs are referred to as "organ meridian access points." Specific emotions are closely tied to corresponding specific elements and, therefore, organs.

HOMEOPATHIC ENERGIZATION PRINCIPLES

Hippocrates was perhaps the first individual to profess and teach that we must look at the spine for the cause of disease. In order to heal the body, we must heal the mind. To heal the mind, we must heal the body. He also alluded to, and perhaps was the precursor, of modern homeopathy.

One of Hippocrates' major activities was to establish a school for physicians. Perhaps this is one of the major reasons he is sometimes referred to as the "Father of Medicine."

In 400 B.C., the first known reference to what would later become known as homeopathy, contained some writings of Hippocrates. In those writings, there were references to agents that caused disease also being capable of helping to overcome the same disease.

The writings of Paracelsus, in the 16th century, also referred to the idea of homeopathy. He suggested that diseases were caused by certain agents that, in other circumstances, could treat them. He purported the disease, and the medicine to treat it, should have the same name.

It was only, however, through the work of Samuel Hahneman in the late 18th and early 19th centuries that this practice has become applicable today. In 1796, Hahneman first wrote about the "similia principle." At that same time he introduced the term "Homeopathy."

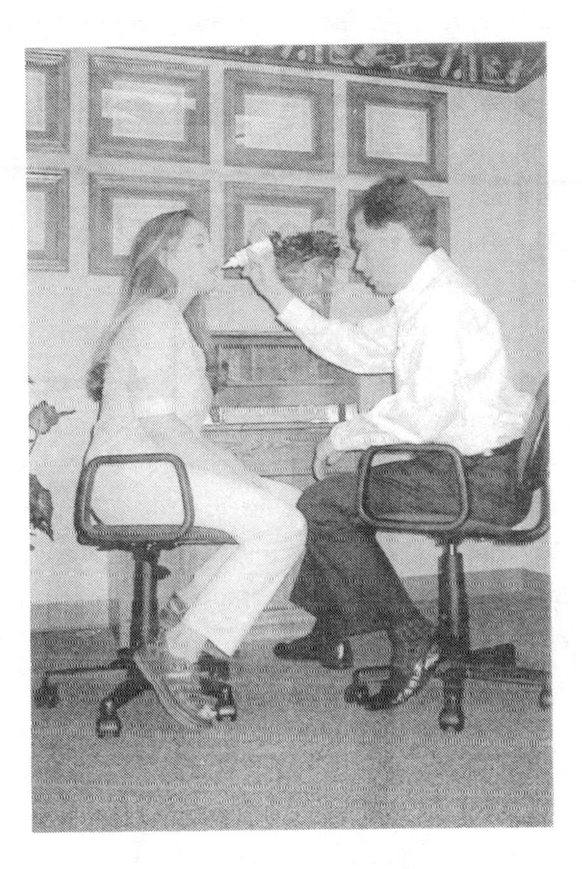

Doctor Administering a Homeopathic NET Remedy

In 1810, Hahneman's book *Organon of the Art of Healing,* was published in Torgaou, Germany. He was an extremely prominent medical author and physician of the time. He was well-known and many quickly sought to read his book.

Once the book was read, however, the European medical community was thrown into tumult as it introduced an entirely new and radical system of medicine which was fundamentally in opposition to the traditional medicine of the time.

Hahneman called his new medicine "Homeopathy." The name was derived from the Greek word "omeos," meaning "similar," and "pathos," meaning "suffering." Homeopathy is a very highly systematic method to powerfully stimulate the body's own ability to cure illness. It is based on a few simple, yet profoundly insightful, principles of Nature which are contrary to today's commonly-held beliefs. In his book, Hahneman laid out the laws and principles of his science, which he had gathered, empirically, over a twenty year period. They are as follows:

1. **A medical cure is brought about in accordance with certain laws of healing that occur in nature.**
2. **Nobody can cure outside these laws.**
3. **There are no diseases as such, only diseased individuals.**
4. **An illness is always dynamic by nature, so the remedy too must therefore be in a dynamic state if it is to cure.**

5. **The patient needs only one particular remedy and no other at any given stage of his illness. Unless that certain remedy is found, he is not cured, but, at best, the condition is only temporarilly relieved.**

At the time of this writing, Dr. Walker has developed eleven Neuro Emotional Technique homeopathic remedies, better known as NET Remedies. These are safe, natural, fast acting, clinically effective, and contain no contra-indicators or side effects. The first five NET Remedies are named for the specific elemental corrections:

#1	**Earth**	**for stomach, spleen, pancreas**
#2	**Metal**	**for lungs and large intestine**
#3	**Water**	**for kidneys and bladder**
#4	**Wood**	**for liver and gall bladder**
#5	**Fire**	**for heart, small intestine, thyroid, adrenals, sex organs**

Additional Net Remedies which are developed to support the healing process are:

#6	**Para Solve**	**for para bowel**
#7	**Flora Plus**	**for bowel flora**
#8	**Allergy**	**for allergies**

#9 ER911	**for acute emotional reaction**
#10 Scars-Adhesions	**for any joint, scar, or myofascial involvement**
#11 Visceral Polarity	**for brain, emotions, ICV (Ilio-cecal valve) allergy, polarity**

Over the decades dramatic environmental changes have occurred and are indicative of the great demand for these formulas to meet the needs of today's health care problems.

* * * * * * * * * *

I have attempted to present a brief background, a "bridging to this breakthrough of Neuro Emotional Anti-sabotage Technique. If the previous chapters have appeared unclear, be assured that the clinical application of NET and NEAT, though complex, is actually quite simple.

The cases presented herein are all true experiences and results of the application of NET and NEAT. All patient names have been changed to protect their privacy. Some of the NET and NEAT doctors who treated these patients have given permission for the use of their names and have been presented.

I salute and honor each NET/NEAT doctor as she/he goes about her/his business of helping people, healing, and therefore creating a

better world in which to live. We do so by creating balance out of chaos.

I salute and honor the O.N.E. Foundation, its faithful and dedicated members who freely give of their time, energy, and money to promote NET/NEAT, the necessary research, and the provision for the Well-Being of this planet.

And last, but certainly not least, I "tip my hat" with the deepest appreciation, honor, respect, and gratitude to Drs. Scott and Deborah Walker. Through many years of vision, dedication, perseverance, toil, sweat, and exacting science, Dr. "Scott" as the visionary, and Dr. "Deb" as the organizer have brought this hurting, suffering world of humanity a powerful and marvelous gift. Indeed...it is...

GOOD NEWS FOR PEOPLE WHO HURT!

(And It Is N.E.A.T.!)

A PORTRAIT OF THE FULLY ALIVE HUMAN BEING

"It would seem that the amount of destructiveness to be found in individuals is proportionate to the amount to which expansiveness of life is curtailed. By this we do not refer to individual frustrations of this or that instinctive desire, but to the thwarting of the whole of life, the blockage of spontaneity of the growth of expression of man's sensuous, emotional, and intellectual capacities. Life has an inner dynamism of its own; it tends to grow, to be expressed, to be lived. It seems that if this tendency is thwarted, the energy directed towards life undergoes a process of decomposition and changes into energies directed towards destruction. In other words, the drive for life and the drive for destruction are not mutually independent factors, but are in a reversed interdependence. The more the drive towards life is thwarted, the stronger is the drive towards destruction; the more life is realized, the less is the strength of destructiveness. Destructiveness is the outcome of unlived life."

Erich Fromm, *Escape From Freedom*

BIBLIOGRAPHY/REFERENCES

Breggan, Peter, *Toxic Psychiatry,* St Martin's Press, New York, NY, 1991

Chopra, Deepak, *Escaping the Prison of the Intellect,* Audio Cassette, New World Library

Connelly, Dianne M., *Traditional Acupuncture: The Law of the Five Elements,* Traditional Acupuncture Institute, Columbia, Maryland, 1979

***Course in Miracles,* Foundation For Inner Peace, Tiburon, CA, 1975**

Dossey, Larry, *Healing Words,* Harper of San Francisco, Harper Collins, 1993

Dyer, Wayne, *Everyday Wisdom,* Hay House, Inc., 1993

Fischman, Walter and Grinims, Mark, *Muscle Response Test,* Richard Marek Publishers, NY, NY, 1979

Fromm, Erich, *The Art of Loving,* Bantam Books, Harper & Row, NY, 1967

Fromm, Erich, *Escape From Freedom, Farrar & Rinehart, Inc., NY, NY, 1941*

Grinder, Michael, *One Man's Journey,* Celestial Arts, Millbrae, CA, 1975

Gibran, Kahlil, *I Care About Your Happiness,* Continental Publications, 1975

Hay, Louise, L., *You Can Heal Your Life,* Hay House, Santa Monica, CA, 1984

Janiger, Oscar & Goldberg, Phillip, *A Different Kind of Healing,* Jeremy P. Tarcher/Putnam's Sons Pub., NY, NY, 1993

Justice, Blair, *Who Gets Sick,* Jeremy P. Tarcher, Los Angeles, CA, 1987

Locke, Steven & Colligan, Douglas, *The Healing Within, The Medicine of Mind and Body,* E. P. Dutton, NY, NY, 1986

May, Rollo, *Man's Search For Himself,* W. W. Norton Co., NY, NY, 1953

Menninger, Karl, *Love Against Hate,* Harcourt, Brace & World, Inc., NY, NY, 1942

Ornstein, Robert & Sobel, David, *The Healing Brain,* Simon & Schuster, NY, NY, 1987

Rossi, Ernest L. & Cheek, David B., *Mind-Body Therapy Healing,* W. W. Norton & Co., NY, NY, 1986

Saraydarian, Torkom, *I Was,* Aquarian Educational Group, 1981

St. Paul, *The New English Bible,* Cambridge, University Press, USA, 1970

Swedenborg, Emanuel, *Heaven and Hell,* Swedenborg Foundation, Inc., 1976

Vithoulkas, George, *Homeopathy Medicine of the New Man,* Simon & Schuster, 1979

Walsch, Neale Donald, *Conversations With God,* G. P. Putnam's Sons, 1996

Williamson, Marianne, *The Healing of America,* Simon & Schuster, NY, NY, 1997

<u>"IF WE DON'T LEAD THIS COUNTRY</u>

<u>(AND EVENTUALLY THE WORLD) TO</u>

<u>THE TRUTH OF THE NATURAL INNATE</u>

<u>HEALING ABILITIES OF THE BODY,</u>

<u>WHO WILL?"</u>

Dr. Scott Walker